THE PREMIER LEAGUE QUIZ BOOK

600 FUN QUESTIONS FOR ALL PREMIER LEAGUE FANS

JAMES CONRAD

Published by Blue Yonder Books

James Conrad has asserted his moral right to be identified as the author of this work in accordance with the Copyright, Designs and Patents Act 1988.

Introduction

*That's the beauty of sport. Sometimes you laugh,
sometimes you cry. Pep Guardiola*

How well do you know the history of the Premier League from its start in 1992 to the present day? Here is your opportunity to find out and test friends and family as well.

This book has 600 questions on the Premier League covering every season since its inception. The questions cover different ranges of obscurity so will be a test for all.

The Premier League Quiz Book is both entertaining and informative and will provide hours of memory wracking fun for Supporters of the Premier League

TABLE OF CONTENTS

Quiz 1: 1992 – 93 Season

1. **1992 – 93 was the first season of the Premier League. Who won the last First Division Championship?**

   a) Leeds United   b) Manchester United   c) Chelsea

2. **How many clubs were there in the first season of the new league?**

   a) 20   b) 22   c) 24

3. **The new league had a 5 year deal with Sky and the BBC. How much was this worth?**

   a) £264m   b) £292m   c) £304m

4. **Which team had won the Second Division Championship in 1991 – 92 thus ensuring promotion to the new Premier League?**

   a) Notts Forest   b) Crystal Palace   c) Ipswich

5. **Who was the manager of this team?**

   a) John Lyall   b) Paul Goddard   c) Bobby Robson

6. **Blackburn finished 6th in Division 2 in 1991 – 92 but were promoted as a result of winning the play offs. Who did**

they beat in the play off at Wembley to clinch the promotion?

a) Derby   b) Leicester   c) Portsmouth

7. **Manchester United won the inaugural Premier League. Who were second?**

a) Liverpool   b) Blackburn   c) Aston Villa

8. **How many points did they win the league by?**

a) 4   b) 10   c) 14

9. **Who scored the first live Premier League goal shown on Sky TV in August 1992?**

a) Alan Shearer   b) Teddy Sheringham   c) Peter Beardsley

10. **Which Premier League ground this season had the lowest gate capacity?**

a) Oldham   b) Queens Park Rangers   c) Southampton

11. **Who was the Arsenal manager this season?**

a) Bruce Rioch   b) Don Howe   c) George Graham

12. **On the 15th February 1993 who was sacked as manager of Chelsea?**

a) Ian Porterfield   b) David Webb   c) Glenn Hoddle

13. **Who scored the first Premier League hat trick?**

a) Allan Shearer   b) Teddy Sheringham   c) Eric Cantona

14. **How many overseas player (non-UK or Irish) were there in the 1992 – 93 Premier League season?**

a) 13   b) 23   c) 33

15. Which team finished bottom of the league this season?

a) Crystal Palace   b) Middlesbrough   c) Notts Forest

16. Who was the Premier League's leading goal scorer in 1992 – 93?

a) Teddy Sheringham   b) Les Ferdinand   c) Alan Shearer

17. Who was the PFA's Players Player of the Year in 1992 - 93?

a) Ryan Giggs   b) Chris Waddle   c) Paul McGrath

18. Which team were top at the turn of the year?

a) Man Utd   b) Arsenal   c) Norwich

19. In February 1993 Arsenal signed a 26 year old Martin Keown from which club?

a) Everton   b) Man City   c) Tottenham

20. Who was second in the list of league goal scorers this season?

a) Alan Shearer   b) Les Ferdinand   c) Dean Holdsworth

Quiz 2: 1993 – 94 Season

1. Who were the new sponsors for the Premier League this season?

a) Barclays   b) Carling   c) Dynorod

2. **Which team promoted from the Football League First Division to the Premier Division in 1993 – 94 were playing in the top league for the first time?**

   a) Swindon   b) Barnsley   c) Reading

3. **On the 28th January 1994 Liverpool sacked their manager. Who was he?**

   a) Kenny Dalglish   b) Roy Evans   c) Graeme Souness

4. **Who won the Premier League in 1993 – 94?**

   a) Man Utd   b) Blackburn   c) Arsenal

5. **Which team scored the most goals in the Premier League this season?**

   a) Man Utd   b) Newcastle   c) Leeds United

6. **Who became the record signing for a goalkeeper this season?**

   a) David James   b) Tim Howard   c) Tim Flowers

7. **Swindon finished bottom of the League and were relegated. How many goals did they concede?**

   a) 90   b) 95   c) 100

8. **Who left Man Utd in May 1994 to move to Middlesbrough?**

   a) Gary Pallister   b) Bryan Robson   c) Keith Gillespie

9. **Wimbledon didn't have their own home ground this season so played at which team's ground?**

   a) West Ham   b) QPR   c) Crystal Palace

10. Who was appointed the Tottenham manager on the 19th June 1993?

    a) Osvaldo Ardiles   b) Steve Perryman c) Gerry Francis

11. Who was the Premier League's leading goal scorer in 1993 – 94?

    a) Alan Shearer b) Andy Cole   c) Chris Sutton

12. On the 22nd September 1994 an 18 year old made their debut for Liverpool. Who was he?

    a) Robbie Fowler   b) Jaime Redknapp   c) Steve McManaman

13. Man Utd also won the FA Cup this season beating Chelsea 4 – 0 in the final. Who were the last team to do the double prior to this?

    a) Tottenham   b) Arsenal   c) Liverpool

14. Arsenal finished 4th and won the European Cup Winners Cup this season. Who was their manager this season?

    a) Arsene Wenger b) Bruce Rioch   c) George Graham

15. Swindon and Oldham were relegated this season. Who was the third club to face the drop?

    a) Southampton   b) Sheff Utd   c) Ipswich

16. Which newly promoted team for this season finished in third place?

    a) Newcastle   b) Blackburn c) Sheffield Wednesday

17. Which team on the last day of the season were losing 2 – 0 to Wimbledon and looking to be relegated, till they turned it around and won 3 – 2 to stay up?

a) Ipswich   b) Southampton   c) Everton

18. Which legend died on January 24th 1994?

a) Sir Matt Busby   b) Bill Shankley   c) Bobby Moore

19. Which team were docked 5 points for financial irregularities after the end of the season?

a) Oldham   b) Swindon   c) Tottenham

20. Who was voted the PFA Player of the Year?

a) Alan Shearer   b) Eric Cantona   c) Peter Beardsley

Quiz 3: 1994 -95 Season

1. In July 1994 Blackburn signed the most expensive player in English football at the time. Who was he?

a) Alan Shearer   b) Chris Sutton   c) Tim Sherwood

2. Blackburn won the Premier League due to the strike partnership of Shearer and Sutton. How many League goals did they get in total?

a) 42   b) 46   c) 49

3. **Man Utd drew their last game 1 -1. If they had won that game they would have won the Premier League again. Who did they draw with?**

   a) Norwich City   b) West Ham   c) Aston Villa

4. **Which newly promoted team finished third in the Premier League?**

   a) Notts Forest   b) Coventry   c) Crystal Palace

5. **How many teams were relegated from the Premier League this season?**

   a) 2   b) 3   c) 4

6. **Manchester United had the biggest win of the season with a 9 -0 victory over whom?**

   a) Crystal Palace   b) Ipswich   c) Norwich

7. **Who did Man Utd buy from Newcastle in January 1995 for £7m?**

   a) Andy Cole   b) Keith Gillespie   c) Gary Pallister

8. **In January 1995 one of the most infamous incidents of the Premier League happened when Eric Cantona 'kung fu kicked' a supporter. Which team was he playing against?**

   a) Everton   b) Crystal Palace   c) Southampton

9. **Another player in trouble this season was Dennis Wise. Who was he convicted of assaulting?**

   a) A journalist   b) A policeman   c)A taxi driver

10. **Which club's ground had the lowest capacity crowd this season?**

   a) Southampton   b) QPR   c) Leicester

11. **Who was the German world cup winner that signed for Tottenham?**

   a) Eike Immel   b) Jurgen Klinsmann   c)Dietmar Hamann

12. **On 21st February 2005 George Graham was sacked as manager of Arsenal. Why was he sacked?**

   a) Poor results   b) Match fixing   c) Bungs

13. **After 13 years Bruce Grobelaar was given a free transfer by Liverpool on the 11th August 1994 to which club?**

   a) Southampton   b) Crystal Palace   c) Brighton

14. **Who scored a hat trick for Liverpool in less than 5 minutes against Arsenal on the 28th August 1994?**

   a) Ian Rush   b) Steve McManaman   c) Robbie Fowler

15. **Who did Man Utd sell to Coventry for £2m in September 1994?**

   a) Paul Ince   b) Dion Dublin   c) Mark Hughes

16. **On the 21st September 1994 who announced their retirement?**

   a) Tony Cottee   b) Tony Cascarino   c) Gary Lineker

17. **On the 5th November 1994 Mike Walker was sacked as manager of Everton. Who took over the hot seat?**

   a) Joe Royle   b) Howard Kendall   c) Walter Smith

18. On the 4th March 1995 who became the first player to score five goals in a Premier League game?

   a) Alan Shearer   b) Andy Cole   c) Stan Collymore

19. Who did Blackburn lose to in the final game of the season, despite which they still won the league?

   a) Chelsea   b) Arsenal   c) Liverpool

20. How many years before was it since Blackburn won the league championship in the top tier?

   a) 62 years   b) 81 years   c) 94 years

Quiz 4: 1995 – 96 Season

1. Who were Premier League Champions in the 1995 – 96 season?

   a) Arsenal   b) Man Utd   c) Aston Villa

2. Dennis Bergkamp was signed by Arsenal in June 1995. Which club was he signed from?

   a) Barcelona   b) Ajax   c) Inter Milan

3. Alan Shearer was the leading goal scorer in the Premier League this season with 31 goals. Who was the second highest scorer?

   a) Ian Wright   b) Les Ferdinand   c) Robbie Fowler

4. **How many hat tricks did Alan Shearer score in this season?**

   a) 3   b) 4   c) 5

5. **Tony Yeboah was the Leeds United centre forward. Where was he born?**

   a) Ghana   b) Ivory Coast   c) Nigeria

6. **Who was the PFA Players' Player of the Year?**

   a) Alan Shearer   b) Les Ferdinand   c) Eric Cantona

7. **Newcastle led the Premier League by how many points at Christmas?**

   a) 6   b) 8   c) 10

8. **Bolton and QPR were relegated. Who was relegated with them?**

   a) Southampton   b) Coventry   c) Man City

9. **In June 1995 Liverpool signed Stan Collymore from which club?**

   a) Sheffield Wednesday   b) Notts Forest   c) Southend

10. **On the 30th June 1995 which world cup winner was appointed as manager of Man City?**

    a) Alan Ball   b) Jack Charlton   c) George Cohen

11. **On the 11th July 1995 who did Arsenal sign from Sampdoria?**

    a) Glenn Helder   b) John Hartson   c) David Platt

12. On the 4th December 1995 who scored a hat trick against Sheffield Wednesday and still finished on the losing team?

   a) Gavin Peacock   b) Dion Dublin   c) Matt Le Tissier

13. Which player created the most assists during the season?

   a) Darren Anderton   b) Eric Cantona   c) Steve McManaman

14. On the 8th April 1996 David Busst sustained a terrible broken leg playing against Man Utd. Which team did he play for?

   a) Southampton   b) Coventry   c) Wimbledon

15. On the 31st January which 17 year old made their debut for West Ham?

   a) Rio Ferdinand   b) Frank Lampard   c) Stan Lazaridis

16. O the 14th February 1996 Bob Paisley died. How many trophies did he win as manager of Liverpool?

   a) 13   b) 17   c) 20

17. On the 30th March 1996 an 18 year old Harry Kewell made his debut for Leeds United. What nationality is he?

   a) American   b) Australian   c) South African

18. On the 15th December 1995, the European Court in the 'Bosman ruling' gave players freedom to leave clubs for no fee at the end of their contract. This was brought by a Belgian player called Bosman. What was his first name?

   a) Jean-Marc   b) Phillipe   c) Leo

19. Who was captain of Man Utd during this Championship and FA Cup winning season?

    a) Eric Cantona   b) Roy Keane   c) Steve Bruce

20. In the 'PFA Team of the Year' who was picked as the goalkeeper?

    a) Peter Schmeichel   b) David James   c) David Seaman

Quiz 5: 1996 – 97 Season

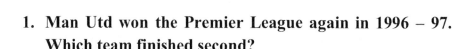

1. Man Utd won the Premier League again in 1996 – 97. Which team finished second?

    a) Liverpool   b) Newcastle   c) Arsenal

2. Middlesbrough signed an Italian player for £7m who got a hat trick against Liverpool on his debut. What was his name?

    a) Massimo Taibi   b) Marco Materazzi   c) Fabrizio Ravanelli

3. Who was sacked as Arsenal manager on the 12th August 1996?

    a) Bruce Rioch   b) Pat Rice   c) George Graham

4. Arsene Wenger took over as full time manager of Arsenal. Which team had he previously managed?

    a) Nancy   b) Monaco   c) Grampus Eight

5. **On the 1st July 1996 Chelsea bought a player who would be a future manager. Who was he?**

a) Ruud Gullit   b) Roberto Di Matteo   c) Gianluca Vialli

6. **On the 14th August 1996 Arsenal sign Patrick Vieira for £3.5m from which club?**

a) AC Milan   b) Inter Milan   c) Juventus

7. **On the opening day of the season David Beckham famously scored a goal from the halfway line in a Man Utd 3 – 0 win. Who were the opponents?**

a) Everton   b) Coventry   c) Wimbledon

8. **Alan Shearer was again the leading scorer in the league. Who was second to him?**

a) Dwight Yorke   b) Robbie Fowler   c) Ian Wright

9. **Who was the Football Writers Association Footballer of the Year?**

a) Alan Shearer   b) Gianfranco Zola   c) Juninho

10. **On the 5th January 1997 Kevin Keegan shocked football by quitting as manager of Newcastle. Who replaced him?**

a) Bobby Robson   b) Osvaldo Ardiles   c) Kenny Dalglish

11. **On the 18th May 1997 who announced their retirement from playing football?**

a) Eric Cantona   b) Ian Rush   c) Bruce Grobbelaar

12. **Middlesbrough were relegated and were two points from safety. However, they had a 3 point deduction January**

which would have saved them. What was the deduction for?

a) Financial irregularities   b) Crowd behaviour   c) Non fulfillment of fixtures

13. **Who became the first foreign manager to win a major trophy this season?**

a) Arsene Wenger   b) Ruud Gullit c) Martin Jol

14. **On the 20th October 1996 Man Utd's 16 game unbeaten run came unstuck with a 5 – 0 thrashing by which team?**

a) Newcastle   b) Liverpool   c) Arsenal

15. **Just six days later Man Utd ship a load more goals with a 6- 3 defeat. Who beat them this time?**

a) Coventry   b) Sunderland c) Southampton

16. **On the 8th November Steve Coppell resigns as manager of Manchester City. How many days was he the manager?**

a) 33 days   b) 46 days c) 53 days

17. **In May 1997 who did Aston Villa pay £7m for?**

a) Dwight Yorke b) Gareth Southgate c) Stan Collymore

18. **On the 6th May 1996 which 17 year old made his debut for Liverpool?**

a) Jaime Carragher b) Michael Owen c) Jason McAteer

19. Gordon Strachan retired as a player after becoming the oldest outfield player to play in the Premier League. How old was he?

    a) 36   b) 38   c) 40

20. Who was the Liverpool captain this season?

    a) John Barnes   b) Mark Wright   c) Neil Ruddock

Quiz 6: 1997 – 98 Season

1. Which team won the Premier League in 1997 – 98?

    a) Man Utd   b) Arsenal   c) Chelsea

2. Who was sacked as the manager of Sheffield Wednesday on the 3rd November 1997?

    a) Ron Atkinson   b) Peter Shreeves   c) David Pleat

3. Bolton, Barnsley and Crystal Palace were promoted to the Premier League this season. How many survived relegation this year?

    a) 0   b) 1   c) 2

4. Three players were the Premier League's leading goal scorers this year with 18 goals. Michael Owen and Chris Sutton were two of them. Who was the third?

    a) Dennis Bergkamp   b) Dion Dublin   c) Andy Cole

5. **Which Chelsea manager, in his first year , won the League Cup and the UEFA Cup Winners Cup**

   a) Jose Mourinho   b) Claudio Ranieri   c) Gianluca Vialli

6. **Who was Liverpool captain in 1997 – 98?**

   a) Paul Ince   b) Jaimie Redknapp   c) Phil Babb

7. **On the 15th July 1997 who did Liverpool sign from Crewe Alexandra?**

   a) Jason McAteer   b) Mark Wright   c) Danny Murphy

8. **On the 1st September 1997 Bolton played their first game at their new Reebok Stadium. What was their old ground called?**

   a) Burnden Park   b) Burndene Park   c) Burdon Park

9. **Newcastle sold Les Ferdinand to which club in July 1997 for £6m?**

   a) Liverpool   b) Blackburn   c) Tottenham

10. **Who did Liverpool sign from Columbus Crew in December 1997?**

    a) Patrik Berger   b) Brad Friedel   c) Karl-Heinz Riedle

11. **The FA were investigating Asian betting syndicates and effects on the Premier League this season. What was the problem?**

    a) The number of 3 – 2 score lines   b) The number of late penalties awarded   c) The floodlights kept going out

12. **Which club became the first former winner of a European Trophy to be relegated to the third tier of their domestic league?**

    a) Derby   b) Manchester City   c) Notts Forest

13. **Which club finished bottom of the Premier League in the 1997 – 98 season?**

    a) Crystal Palace   b) Bolton   c) Barnsley

14. **Who made the most assists in the Premier League in 1997 – 98?**

    a) Dennis Bergkamp   b) David Beckham   c) Teddy Sheringham

15. **Who was the goal keeper in the PFA Team of the Year?**

    a) Peter Schmeichel   b) David Seaman   c) Nigel Martyn

16. **Who were the Arsenal Shirt sponsors this season?**

    a) Dreamcast   b) JVC   c) Fly Emirates

17. **Everton managed to remain in the Premier League on goal difference over Bolton. What happened in the Bolton v Everton game which finished 0 - 0?**

    a) Bolton had a good goal disallowed   b) Bolton should have received a penalty   c) Two Bolton players were sent off

18. **The September Manager of the Month award was won by the Leicester manager. Who was he?**

    a) Peter Taylor   b) Dave Bassett   c) Martin O'Neill

19. **Which Scottish player made the PFA Team of the Year?**

    a) Dominic Matteo   b) Colin Hendry   c) Don Hutchison

20. Who was the West Ham manager this season?

a) Harry Redknapp   b) Trevor Brooking   c) Glenn Roeder

Quiz 7: 1998 – 99 Season

1. **Manchester United won the Premier League in the 1998 – 99 season. How may league games did they lose?**

a) 1   b) 2   c) 3

2. **It was the 100th year of top flight football in England, not counting the war years. There were 4 of the original teams in the Premier League this season. They were Aston Villa, Everton, Blackburn and which other team?**

a) Derby   b) Liverpool   c) Arsenal

3. **Who was sacked as manager of Newcastle on the 27th August 1998?**

a) Ruud Gullit   b) Kenny Dalglish   c) Kevin Keegan

4. **The biggest score of the season was an 8 – 1 drubbing from Man Utd at which club?**

a) Charlton   b) Southampton   c) Notts Forest

5. **Who was the first player to come on as a substitute and score a hat trick in the Premier League this season?**

a) Chris Armstrong   b) Darren Huckerby   c) Ole Gunnar

Solskjaer

6. **Which French player was the PFA Player of the Year?**

   a) David Ginola   b) Patrick Vieira   c) Emmanuel Petit

7. **Which team became the most successful defensively by only conceding 17 league goals all season in 1998 – 99?**

   a) Man Utd   b) Chelsea   c) Arsenal

8. **In August 1998 Newcastle signed a Peruvian from Boca Juniors. Who was he?**

   a) Claudio Pizzaro   b) Nolberto Solano   c) Ysrael Zuniga

9. **Man Utd paid a club record fee for Dwight Yorke in August 1998. Which club did they sign him from?**

   a) Aston Villa   b) Birmingham   c) Blackburn

10. **On the 6th September 1998 who is sacked after 9 months as Tottenham manager?**

   a) Christian Gross   b) Gerry Francis   c) Chris Hughton

11. **Who did they appoint as a replacement on the 1st October 1998?**

   a) David Pleat   b) Glenn Hoddle   c) George Graham

12. **On the 12th September 1998 Man Utd accepted a £623.4m bid from who?**

   a) BSKYB   b) Michael Knighton   c) Malcolm Glazer

13. **In January 1998 which 15 year old schoolboy signed for Arsenal's academy in a £2m deal?**

   a) Ashley Cole   b) Jermaine Pennant   c) Cesc Fabregas

14. On the 30th January 1999 Notts Forest get their first league win of the season with a win at which club?

   a) Coventry   b) Chelsea   c) Everton

15. Who made their debut for Liverpool in November 1998?

   a) Jaimie Carragher   b) Steven Gerrard   c) Michael Owen

16. Three players were top scorers in the Premier League this season with 18 goals. They were Michael Owen, Dwight Yorke and who?

   a) Jimmy Floyd Hasselbaink   b) Dion Dublin   c) Andy Cole

17. Two players had the most assists. One was Dennis Bergkamp. Who was the other?

   a) Jimmy Floyd Hasselbaink   b) David Beckham   c) David Ginola

18. The Charlton Athletic manager was the manager of the month in August and February. Who was he?

   a) Alan Curbishley   b) Iain Dowie   c) Alan Pardew

19. Who was the Premier League Player of the Year?

   a) Jaap Stam   b) Sol Campbell   c) Dwight Yorke

20. There were four Frenchman in the PFA Team of the Year. Three were from Arsenal, but who was the one from Tottenham?

   a) Marcel Desailly   b) Didier Deschamps   c) David Ginola

Quiz 8:1999 – 00 Season

1. **Manchester United won the Premier League in the 1999 – 00 season. How many points did they win it by?**

    a) 14 points   b) 16 points   c) 18 points

2. **Who finished second?**

    a) Arsenal   b) Leeds   c) Liverpool

3. **Coventry finished 14th in the league. How many away games did they win?**

    a) 0   b) 1   c) 2

4. **Which team were relegated after 14 years in the top flight?**

    a) Southampton   b) Wimbledon   c) Newcastle

5. **Who was appointed the manager of Newcastle on the 2nd September 1999?**

    a) Alan Shearer   b) Ruud Gullit   c) Bobby Robson

6. **Man Utd didn't enter the FA Cup so that they could enter the FIFA World Club Championship. Who beat them 3 – 1 at the group stage to knock them out?**

    a) Vasco da Gama   b) Necaxa   c) South Melbourne

7. **Leeds United had a run to the semi-finals of the UEFA Cup and qualified for next season's Champions League. Who was their manager?**

   a) George Graham   b) Terry Venables   c) David O'Leary

8. **Who did Arsenal sell to Real Madrid on 2nd August 1999 for £23m?**

   a) Marc Overmars   b) Emmanuel Petit   c) Nicolas Anelka

9. **The very next day Arsene Wenger bought Thierry Henry from Juventus for how much?**

   a) £11m   b) £22m   c) £33m

10. **Which 19 year old was signed from Wolverhampton by Coventry in a £6m deal?**

    a) Carlton Palmer   b) Chris Kirkland   c) Robbie Keane

11. **On 18th September Newcastle achieve the second highest Premier League score to date with Alan Shearer getting 5 goals. Who was beaten 8 - 0?**

    a) Sheffield Wednesday   b) Derby   c) Watford

12. **Who joined Chelsea in January 2000 in a loan move from AC Milan?**

    a) Marcel Desailly   b) Didier Deschamps   c) George Weah

13. **In May 2000 Man Utd signed Fabien Barthez for a national record fee for a goalkeeper from which club?**

    a) Lyon   b) Monaco   c) Nantes

14. Who was the leading goal scorer in the Premier League in 1999 – 2000 season?

a) Allan Shearer   b) Dwight Yorke   c) Kevin Phillips

15. The Sheffield Wednesday manager won the manager of the month award in January. On the 21st March he was sacked. Who was he?

a) Jim Smith   b) Danny Wilson   c) Paul   Jewell

16. This season the last FA Cup final was played at the old Wembley. Who won it?

a) Chelsea   b) Arsenal   c) Liverpool

17. Who finished bottom of the league?

a) Watford   b) Sheffield Wednesday   c) Wimbledon

18. There were four Man Utd players in the PFA Team of the Year. They were David Beckham, Andy Cole, Roy Keane and who else?

a) Paul Scholes   b) Ryan Giggs   c) Jaap Stam

19. Man City won promotion from Division One to the Premier League in a second successive season of promotion. Who was their manager?

a) Joe Royle   b) Frank Clark   c) Kevin Keegan

20. What was the name of Bradford City's stadium?

a) The Jewson's Stadium   b) The Screwfix   c) Valley Parade

Quiz 9: 2000 – 01 Season

1. **Which team in the Premier League this season played at Highfield Road?**

   a) Bradford   b) Coventry   c) Ipswich

2. **Liverpool achieved a unique treble of cup wins. The won the League Cup, the FA Cup and the UEFA Cup. Who was the manager who took them there?**

   a) Roy Evans   b) Rafa Benitez   c) Gerard Houllier

3. **Who was sacked as manager of Chelsea on the 12th September 2000?**

   a) Gianluca Vialli   b) Claudio Ranieri   c) Ruud Gullit

4. **Who was the PFA Young Player of the Year awarded to this year?**

   a) Michael Owen   b) Jermain Defoe   c) Steven Gerrard

5. **Jimmy Floyd Hasselbaink was the Premier League's leading scorer with 23 goals this season. Who was the second leading scorer?**

   a) Marcus Stewart   b) Thierry Henry   c) Michael Owen

6. On the 30th March 2001 Tottenham signed Glenn Hoddle as manager. Which team did he leave to take over at Spurs?

a) Southampton   b) Swindon   c) Wolverhampton

7. Paul Gascoigne left Middlesbrough on a free transfer and signed for who?

a) Boston   b) Burnley   c) Everton

8. On the 26th October 2000 Leeds United beat the UK transfer record with the £18m signing of who?

a) Rio Ferdinand   b) Robbie Keane   c) Mark Viduka

9. After failing to get into the Spurs side which 19 year old made their debut for QPR on the first day of the season?

a) Jermain Defoe   b) Peter Crouch   c) Ashley Cole

10. Who was the Man Utd captain this season?

a) Denis Irwin   b) Roy Keane   c) Gary Neville

11. Who finished bottom of the Premier League this season?

a) Man City   b) Coventry   c) Bradford

12. Who became the first Australian to score a Premier League hat trick?

a) Mark Viduka   b) Harry Kewell   c) Stan Lazaridis

13. Who was the Premier League manager of the season?

a) Alex Ferguson   b) Arsene Wenger   c) George Burley

14. Who was the Brazilian who made the PFA Team of the Year?

a) Sylvinho   b) Juninho   c) Branco

15. Which footballer won the PFA Player's Player of the Year and the Football Writers 'Footballer of the Year'?

a) Patrick Vieira   b) Teddy Sheringham   c) Jaap Stam

16. On the 21st August 2000 Paulo Wanchope scored a hat trick for Man City against Sunderland. Where was Paulo Wanchope born?

a) The Cameroons   b) Ivory Coast   c) Costa Rica

17. In winning the League Cup final against Leicester in February 2001 Liverpool became the first English team to do what?

a) Win the League Cup outright   b) Win a major trophy on penalties   c) Win 50 trophies in their history

18. On the 21st May 2001 Leeds United bought who from Inter Milan from for £12m?

a) Jonathan Woodgate   b) Oliver Dacourt   c) Robbie Keane

19. On the 14th June 2001 who did Chelsea pay £11m for?

a) Frank Lampard   b) William Gallas   c) Graeme Le Saux

20. Manchester United won the title for the third season in a row. How many teams had won the English League title for three years in a row before this?

a) 2   b) 3   c) 4

Quiz 10: 2001 – 02 Season

1. **Who were the Premier League sponsors this season?**

   a) Barclaycard   b) Carling   c) Nationwide

2. **There were only two Englishman in the PFA Team of the Year for 2001 – 02. One was Rio Ferdinand. Which Southampton player was the other?**

   a) Matt Le Tissier   b) Kevin Davies   c) Wayne Bridge

3. **Arsenal won the League and FA Cup this season. How many times had they done this before?**

   a) 1   b) 2   c) 3

4. **What record did Arsenal set in winning the Premier League in 2001 – 02?**

   a) They scored in every Premier League game   b) They were unbeaten away from home   c) They won their last 13 games in the league

5. **On the 12th July 2001 Man Utd broke the English transfer fee record with a £28.1m signing of who?**

   a) Juan Sebastian Veron   b) Ruud van Nistelrooy   c) Diego Forlan

6. **On the 29th November 2001 Liverpool sold Robbie Fowler to which club?**

   a) Man City   b) North Queensland Fury   c) Leeds

7. **On the 15th March 2002 Everton appointed David Moyes as manager. Which club had he been at prior to this?**

   a) Bury   b) Huddersfield   c) Preston North End

8. **In August 2001 Liverpool signed which goalkeeper from Feyenoord?**

   a) Sander Westerveld   b) Jerzy Dudek   c) Pepe Reina

9. **In September 2001 Man Utd signed veteran Laurent Blanc from which club?**

   a) Inter Milan   b) Barcelona   c) Marseille

10. **Ipswich were relegated but still qualified for the UEFA Cup. Why was this?**

    a) They were runners up in the FA Cup   b) They were runners up in the League   c) They won the Fair Play League

11. **On the 19th February 2002 a future Chelsea manager retired from playing. Who was he?**

    a) Roberto Di Matteo   b) Antonio Conte   c) Andre Villas Boas

12. **Which 17 year old made their debut for Middlesbrough in April 2002?**

    a) Darren Bent   b) Stewart Downing   c) Mark Crossley

13. Who took over as manager of Aston Villa on the 5th February 2002?

a) Jim Smith   b) John Gregory   c) Graham Taylor

14. Who was Aston Villa's captain this season?

a) Dion Dublin   b) Paul Merson   c) Darius Vassell

15. Who was the leading league goal scorer for the season?

a) Thierry Henry   b) Ruud van Nistelrooy   c) Alan Shearer

16. On the 8th February 2002 who did Newcastle buy from Notts Forest for £5m?

a) Craig Bellamy   b) Robbie Elliot   c) Jermaine Jenas

17. Who was the Chelsea captain this season?

a) Gianfranco Zola   b) Frank Lampard   c) Marcel Desailly

18. In August 2001 Man Utd sold Jaap Stam to which club?

a) Lazio   b) AC Milan   c) Inter Milan

19. West Bromwich Albion were promoted this year into the 2002 – 03 Premier League. One of their wins was an abandoned game at Sheffield United. Why was it abandoned?

a) Floodlight failure   b) The goals were the wrong size   c) Sheffield United had too few players on the pitch

20. Who was the 'Premier League Player of the Season'?

a) Freddie Ljunberg   b) Ryan Giggs   c) Thierry Henry

Quiz 11: 2002 – 03 Season

1. **Arsenal had scored in a record 55 consecutive games, but this ended on the 7th December 2002. Which team ended their run?**

    a) Liverpool   b) Man Utd   c) Chelsea

2. **Fulham were unable to play their home games at Craven Cottage as it was being refurbished. Where did they play their home games?**

    a) Boleyn Ground   b) The Valley   c) Loftus Road

3. **Newcastle signed a 20 year old from Ipswich for £5m in July 2002. Who was he?**

    a) Shola Ameobi   b) Titus Bramble   c) Kieron Dyer

4. **Man Utd won the Premier League for the eighth time in eleven years. Who came second?**

    a) Arsenal   b) Newcastle   c) Chelsea

5. **On the 19th October 2002 who became the youngest scorer to date in the Premier League, scoring five days before his 17th birthday?**

    a) James Milner   b) Cesc Fabregas   c) Wayne Rooney

6. **On the 16th February 2003 a notorious incident happened in the Man Utd changing room when Sir Alex**

Ferguson accidentally injured David Beckham when he kicks some boots in frustration. Which team had caused the frustration by beating them that day?

a) Arsenal   b) Chelsea   c) Newcastle

7. **In January 2003 Chelsea were fined £5,000. Why did they incur a fine?**

a) Arrived late for a game   b) Interest on a previous fine   c) State of the pitch

8. **On the 21st January 2003 Newcastle bought who from financially troubled Leeds United for £9m?**

a) Michael Bridges   b) Lee Bowyer   c) Johnathan Woodgate

9. **At the end of March Leeds United sacked their manager. Who was he?**

a) David O'Leary   b) Terry Venables   c) George Graham

10. **Sunderland were relegated with 19 points having lost their last 15 games. How many goals did they score all season?**

a) 15   b) 21   c) 24

11. **How many managers did Sunderland have during this relegation season?**

a) 1   b) 2   c) 3

12. **West Ham were also relegated with a record number of points for a relegated team in the 20 team format. How many points did they get?**

a) 38   b) 40   c) 42

13. Who were Liverpool's shirt sponsor this season?

a) Carlsberg   b) Standard Charter   c) Crown Paints

14. Who was the Arsenal captain in 2003 – 03?

a) Patrick Vieira   b) Sol Campbell   c) Martin Keown

15. Who was the leading Premier League scorer in 2002 – 03?

a) Michael Owen   b) Thierry Henry   c) Ruud van Nistelrooy

16. Which team had the most clean sheets in this season?

a) Arsenal   b) Blackburn   c) Man Utd

17. On the 11th August 2002 who retired after a 19 year career?

a) David Seaman   b) Peter Schmeichel   c) Tony Adams

18. On the 17th June 2003 who did Man Utd sell for £25m?

a) David Beckham   b) Juan Veron   c) Diego Forlan

19. In the 2002 – 03 season what was Bolton's stadium called?

a) The Macron Stadium   b) The Reebok Stadium   c) The University of Bolton Stadium

20. Man City played their last game at Maine Road on the 11th May 2003. They lost 1 – 0 to which team?

a) Arsenal   b) Charlton   c) Southampton

Quiz 12: 2003 – 04 Season

1. **Arsenal finished the season unbeaten in the Premier League. How many draws did they get in the league?**

   a) 10   b) 12   c) 14

2. **Who were the only other team to have ever finished a season unbeaten?**

   a) Wolverhampton   b) Wanderers   c) Preston North End

3. **Who finished second to the Arsenal 'Invincibles'?**

   a) Chelsea   b) Man Utd   c) Liverpool

4. **On the 14th August 2003 Chelsea signed a player from Parma for £15.8m. They would end up sacking him and suing for compensation. Who was he?**

   a) Filipe Oliveira   b) Hernan Crespo   c) Adrian Mutu

5. **An English manager won a major trophy this season, the first since Brian Little's Aston Villa won the League Cup in 1996. Who was it?**

   a) Steve McClaren   b) Steve Bruce   c) Sam Allardyce

6. **The three promoted teams this year were Leicester, Portsmouth and Wolves. Which was the only one not to get relegated back this season?**

   a) Leicester   b) Portsmouth   c) Wolves

7. **Who was sacked as Spurs manager on 22nd September 2003?**

   a) George Graham   b) Glenn Hoddle   c) David Pleat

8. **Who was the PFA Young Player of the Year?**

   a) Wayne Rooney   b) John Terry   c) Scott Parker

9. **The Manager of the Month award was won twice by Arsene Wenger in August and February. Who else won it twice this season?**

   a) Sam Allardyce   b) Sir Alex Ferguson   c) Claudio Ranieri

10. **Who was the goalkeeper that Man Utd signed on 15th July 2003 for £2.3m?**

    a) Edwin van der Saar   b) Tim Howard   c) Roy Carroll

11. **Rio Ferdinand was banned for 8 months on the 19th December 2003. Why was he suspended?**

    a) Missed drugs tests   b) Betting   c) Revelations in autobiography

12. **In February 2004 Tottenham bought a 22 year old for £7m from another London club. Who was he?**

    a) Ledley King   b) Robbie Kean   c) Jermain Defoe

13. **On the 16th May 2004 Arsenal signed Robin van Persie from which club for £2.75m**

    a) Feyenoord   b) Ajax   c) Juventus

14. **On the 16th June 2004 who became the Liverpool manager?**

    a) Gerard Houllier   b) Rafa Benitez   c) Roy Hodgson

15. On the 2nd June 2004 the 'Special One' became manager of Chelsea. Who was Mourinho's predecessor at Chelsea?

   a) Claudio Ranieri   b) Avram Grant   c) Luiz Felipe Scolari

16. Arsenal were prevented from doing the double by being knocked out in the semi-finals by the eventual winners. Who beat them?

   a) Chelsea   b) Liverpool   c) Man Utd

17. In January 2004 which former England goalkeeper retired?

   a) Nigel Martyn   b) Dave Beasant   c) David Seaman

18. Who was the leading goal scorer in the Premier League this season?

   a) Alan Shearer   b) Thierry Henry   c) Louis Saha

19. Chelsea signed many players this season including Hernan Crespo. What nationality is he?

   a) Peruvian   b) Brazilian   c) Argentinian

20. How many players did Arsenal have in the Team of the Year, and can you name them?

   a) 4   b) 5   c) 6

Quiz 13: 2004 – 05 Season

1. **Chelsea won the Premier League in 2004 – 05 with a record points haul for the time. How many points did they get?**

   a) 93   b) 95   c) 97

2. **In June 2004 Tottenham appointed Jacques Santini as manager. How many games did he last?**

   a) 13   b) 15   c) 17

3. **Which team was the first to be bottom of the league on Christmas Day and avoid relegation?**

   a) West Brom   b) Southampton   c) Norwich

4. **Arsenal's record breaking run of unbeaten games came to an end on the 24th October 2004. Who beat them?**

   a) Liverpool   b) Chelsea   c) Man Utd

5. **Who were Newcastle's shirt sponsor this season?**

   a) Wonga   b) Northern Rock   c) 888.com

6. **Who was appointed the Manchester City manager on the 21st March 2005?**

   a) Kevin Keegan   b) Mark Hughes   c) Stuart Pearce

7. **On the 31st August 2004 Man Utd paid a world record fee for a teenager when they bought Wayne Rooney from Everton. How much did they pay?**

   a) £27m   b) £37m   c) £47m

8. **The day before this on the 30th August 2004 Newcastle sacked their manager. Who was sacked?**

   a) Graeme Souness   b) Glenn Roeder   c) Sir Bobby Robson

9. **On the 1st April 2005 two Newcastle players were sent off against Aston Villa for fighting each other. One was Lee Bowyer, who was the other?**

   a) Jermaine Jenas   b) Kieron Dyer   c) Craig Bellamy

10. **On the 25th May Liverpool won the European Cup in the 'Miracle of Istanbul' coming back from 3 – 0 down to win on penalties. Who did they beat?**

    a) Inter Milan   b) Juventus   c) AC Milan

11. **Who was Tottenham's captain this season?**

    a) Robbie Kean   b) Ledley King   c) Michael Carrick

12. **Who finished bottom of the Premier League in 2004 – 05?**

    a) Southampton   b) Norwich   c) Crystal Palace

13. **How many goals did Chelsea concede in the league this year?**

    a) 15   b) 17   c) 19

14. **Arsenal won the Fair Play Award this season. One of their former players however gained the most yellow**

cards for the season with 11. Who was the offending player?

a) Jermaine Pennant   b) Matthew Upson   c) Ray Parlour

15. **Where was Patrick Vieira born?**

a) Senegal   b) France   c) Belgium

16. **Among many records set by Chelsea this season was the most away wins. How many did they get?**

a) 13   b) 14   c) 15

17. **Who were the one team to get a league win over Chelsea in 2004 – 05?**

a) Everton   b) Man City   c) Liverpool

18. **Who got the Golden Boot for the Premier League by scoring the most goals?**

a) Alan Shearer   b) Robert Pires   c) Thierry Henry

19. **This was the inaugural season for the Golden Glove award to the goalkeeper with the most clean sheets. Who was the first winner?**

a) Pepe Reina   b) Tim Howard   c) Petr Cech

20. **Who won the Fair Play Award for 2004 – 05 for the best behaved and most sporting team?**

a) Arsenal   b) Tottenham   c) Blackburn

Quiz 14: 2005 – 06 Season

1. **This was Wigan's first season in the Premier League. What year were they first elected to play in the Football League?**

   a) 1962   b) 1973   c) 1978

2. **Who won the Premier League in 2005 – 06?**

   a) Chelsea   b) Man Utd   c) Arsenal

3. **Sunderland finished bottom of the league with 15 points. How many home games did they win?**

   a) 0   b) 1   c) 2

4. **Who achieved a record of 106 points this season to earn promotion from the Football League Championship to the Premier League?**

   a) Reading   b) Watford   c) Sheff Utd

5. **Some Manchester United supporters who were disgruntled at the Glazers takeover formed their own club. What was it called?**

   a) FC United   b) FC Manchester United   c) FC United of Manchester

6. **Who was the 18 year old that Tottenham bought from Leeds United for £1m on the 1st July 2005?**

   a) Jermaine Jenas   b) Arran Lennon   c) Robbie Keane

7. **On the 15th July 2005 which Arsenal legend left after nine years at the club?**

   a) Patrick Vieira   b) Dennis Bergkamp   c) Thierry Henry

8. **Liverpool won the UEFA Super Cup on the 26th August 2005. Who did they beat?**

   a) Monaco   b) Malmo   c) CSKA Moscow

9. **On the 29th August 2005 Manchester United became the first team to achieve what?**

   a) Get 1,000 points in the Premier League   b) Score 1,000 Premier League goals   b) Get 1,000 yellow cards in the Premier League

10. **Who was the 16 year old that Arsenal bought from Southampton for £5m on the 20th January 2006?**

    a) Cesc Fabregas   b) Emmanuel Adebayor   c) Theo Walcott

11. **On the 18th February 2006 Liverpool beat Man Utd in the FA Cup. When was the last time this happened?**

    a) 1921   b) 1961   c) 1991

12. **Chelsea won 18 of their 19 home games and drew the other. Which team held Chelsea 1 – 1 at Stamford Bridge?**

    a) Middlesbrough   b) Charlton   c) Fulham

13. Who was Arsenal's captain this season?

a) Robert Pires   b) Freddie Ljungberg   c) Thierry Henry

14. Who was the Tottenham manager this season?

a) Jacques Santini   b) Martin Jol   c) Harry Redknapp

15. Which Wigan player was in the PFA Team of the Year in the 2005 – 06 season?

a) Henri Camara   b) Leighton Baines   c) Pascal Chimbonda

16. Who won the PFA Golden Glove award for 2005 – 06?

a) Pepe Reina   b) Petr Cech   c) Tim Howard

17. What was Wigan's ground called?

a) Springfield Park   b) JJB Stadium   c) DW Stadium

18. Chelsea's unbeaten 41 game run in the league was ended in November 2005 by which team?

a) Arsenal   b) Liverpool   c) Man Utd

19. This was Arsenal's final season at Highbury. Who did they play in their final game at the stadium?

a) Charlton   b) Wigan   c) Tottenham

20. Sunderland finished with 15 points to beat the previous record for the lowest points total. Whose total did they beat?

a) Sunderland   b) Reading   c) Barnsley

Quiz 15: 2006 – 07 Season

1. **The PFA Team of the Year for 2006 – 07 had no less than eight Man Utd players in it. Which one of these was not one of the eight?**

   a) Patrice Evra   b) Gary Neville   c) Dimitar Berbatov

2. **On the 8th August 2006 Gary Taylor-Fletcher scored a goal for Huddersfield. In the history of the English Premier League and Football league what number goal was this?**

   a) 100,000th b) 250,000th c) 500,000th

3. **On the 14th October 2006 Petr Cech received a depressed fracture of the skull during a game which necessitated him wearing his balaclava style head protection in future games. Who was he playing against?**

   a) Reading   b) Liverpool   c) Charlton

4. **The three promoted teams to the Premier League did not fare very well and only one wasn't relegated. Which one?**

   a) Watford   b) Reading   c) Sheffield United

5. **Who were Man Utd's shirt sponsor this season?**

   a) AIG   b) Vodafone   c) Chevrolet

6. **Which club did Jimmy Floyd Hasselbaink play for this season?**

   a) Chelsea   b) Middlesbrough   c) Charlton

7. **Reading had one player who played in the 2006 World Cup, Ulises De La Cruz. Which country did he play for?**

   a) Peru   b) Ecuador   c) Chile

8. **There are 20 teams in the Premier League. How many league games does this result in each season?**

   a) 340   b) 360   c) 380

9. **Who was the Aston Villa captain in the 2006 – 07 season?**

   a) Chris Sutton   b) Gareth Barry   c) Gabriel Agbonlahor

10. **Which team had the fewest losses in 2006 – 07?**

    a) Man Utd   b) Chelsea   c) Arsenal

11. **Who was the leading goal scorer in this season?**

    a) Didier Drogba   b) Wayne Rooney   c) Cristiano Ronaldo

12. **On the 17th March 2007 which Premier League goalkeeper scored a goal?**

    a) Brad Friedel   b) Peter Schmeichel   c) Paul Robinson

13. **There was controversy on the last day of the season when West Ham beat Man Utd 1 – 0, which guaranteed their survival, with the winner scored by an ineligible player. Who was that player?**

    a) Luis Boa Morte   b) Carlos Tevez   c) Lee Bowyer

14. **On the 28th July 2006 Man Utd sold Ruud van Nistelrooy to which club for £10.2m?**

   a) Barcelona   b) Ajax   c) Real Madrid

15. **On the 30th December 2006 Moritz Voiz scored for Fulham against Chelsea. This was a milestone goal for the Premier League. Which milestone was it?**

   a) 10,000th goal   b) 15,000th goal   c) 20,000th goal

16. **Who was the Man City manager this season?**

   a) Kevin Keegan   b) Sven-Goran Eriksson   c) Stuart Pearce

17. **Chelsea won the FA Cup in 2007. Who did they beat 1 – 0?**

   a) Man Utd   b) Arsenal   c) Fulham

18. **Who won the Golden Glove for the most clean sheets in this season?**

   a) Pepe Reina   b) Tim Howard   c) Marcus Hahnemann

19. **What nationality is Tim Howard?**

   a) Scottish   b) Canadian   c) American

20. **Which team achieved the highest winning margin of the season by thrashing West Ham 6 – 0?**

   a) Arsenal   b) Chelsea   c) Reading

Quiz 16: 2007 – 08 Season

—————— ❧ ——————

1. **How many wins did Derby achieve in the 2007 – 08 season?**

   a) 1   b) 2   c) 3

2. **Manchester United won the title by 2 points with a 2 – 0 win in the last game of the season. Who did they beat in this final game?**

   a) Reading   b) Birmingham   c) Wigan

3. **The runners up created a new record of for the most points achieved by the runner up club. Which club was this?**

   a) Liverpool   b) Chelsea   c) Arsenal

4. **In December 2007, for the first time in the Premier League, two players from opposing teams scored hat tricks. Roque Santa Cruz for Blackburn. Who got three goals for Wigan in their 5 – 3 victory?**

   a) Marlon King   b) Emile Heskey   c) Marcus Bent

5. **A player managed to score a hat trick against Derby in both the home and away fixture, the first time it had been done in the Premier League. Who achieved this?**

   a) Emmanuel Adebayor   b) Fernando Torres   c) Cristiano Ronaldo

6. **A player became the first Portsmouth player to make the PFA Team of the Year this season. Who was this?**

   a) Milan Baros   b) Sol Campbell   c) David James

7. **On the 28th August 2007 Ole Gunnar Solskjaer retired from playing at the age of 34. What nationality is he?**

   a) Norwegian   b) Swedish   c) Danish

8. **On the 20th September 2007 Jose Mourinho resigned as Chelsea manager after falling out with Roman Abramovich. Who took over the Chelsea hot seat?**

   a) Guus Hiddink   b) Luiz Felipe Scolari   c) Avram Grant

9. **In January 2008 Sam Allardyce was sacked as Newcastle manager. Who takes over this hot seat?**

   a) Kevin Keegan   b) Chris Hughton   c) Alan Pardew

10. **What nationality was Sunderland's manager during the 2007 – 08 season?**

    a) English   b) Scottish   c) Irish

11. **In February 2008 Tottenham won their first trophy in 9 years when they win the League Cup. Who did they beat 2 – 1?**

    a) Chelsea   b) Fulham   c) Middlesbrough

12. **On the 29th April 2008 Tottenham signed Luca Modric for £16.5m from which Croatian club**

    a) Hadjuk Split   b) Dinamo Zagreb   c) Osijek

13. On the 26th November 2007 Wigan paid Birmingham a then record £3m to sign their manager. Who was he?

   a) Steve Bruce   b) Juande Ramos   c) Paul Jewell

14. On the 11th May 2008 Middlesbrough had the biggest winning margin of the season when they won 8 – 1. Who were the unfortunate victims?

   a) Wigan   b) Sunderland   c) Man City

15. Who won the Golden Boot in 2007 – 08?

   a) Cristiano Ronaldo   b) Fernando Torres   c) Dimitar Berbatov

16. Which club had the lowest average home attendance this season?

   a) Portsmouth   b) Wigan   c) Fulham

17. On the 23rd July 2007 Freddie Ljungberg left Arsenal after nearly 9 years. Which club did he go to?

   a) West Ham   b) Real Madrid   c) Inter Milan

18. How many red cards were issued in the Premier League this season?

   a) 55   b) 61   c) 66

19. Which player had the most assists in 2007 – 08?

   a) Cesc Fabregas   b) Ashley Young   c) Wayne Rooney

20. Who did Fulham appoint as manager on the 30th December 2007?

   a) Mark Hughes   b) Chris Coleman   c) Roy Hodgson

Quiz 17: 2008 – 09 Season

1. **This season the rule on the number of substitutes on the bench was changed. How many were you allowed in the 2008 – 09 season?**

   a) 5   b) 6   c) 7

2. **Man Utd won the title but were beaten home and away by the second placed team. Who came second?**

   a) Liverpool   b) Arsenal   c) Chelsea

3. **Guus Hiddink was appointed the manager of Chelsea on the 11th February 2009. He also continued as the manager of which national team?**

   a) Belarus   b) Switzerland   c) Russia

4. **Arsenal were involved in two 4 – 4 draws this season. One was with Liverpool. Who were the opponents in the other game?**

   a) Man Utd   b) Tottenham   c) Fulham

5. **West Brom, Stoke and Hull were the three teams who were promoted to the Premier League this season. Which was the only one that was relegated?**

   a) West Brom   b) Stoke   c) Hull

6. **Aston Villa beat Man City 4 – 2 on the 17th August 2008. Which Villa player got a hat trick in 7 minutes and 3 seconds, the quickest hat trick of the season?**

   a) Emile Heskey   b) John Carew   c) Gabriel Agbonlahor

7. **Who won the Golden Boot in 2008 – 09?**

   a) Cristiano Ronaldo   b) Nicolas Anelka   c) Fernando Torres

8. **Who became West Ham's first non-UK manager on the 11th September 2008?**

   a) Avram Gran   b) Slaven Bilic   c) Gianfranco Zola

9. **On the 1st September 2008, with seconds to go in the summer transfer window, Manchester City signed who for £32.5m?**

   a) Vincent Kompany   b) Robinho   c) Pablo Zabaleta

10. **Who was the Portsmouth captain in the 2008 – 09 season?**

    a) Sylvain Distin   b) Sol Campbell   c) David James

11. **Who did Tottenham sign as manager on the 26th October 2008?**

    a) Harry Redknapp   b) Andre Villas-Boas   c) Tim Sherwood

12. **Which team had the fewest losses in 2008 – 09?**

    a) Man Utd   b) Liverpool   c) Chelsea

13. **Steve Sidwell scored the quickest goal of the season on the 7th December 2008 in 31 seconds. Which club did he play for?**

    a) Everton   b) Fulham   c) Aston Villa

14. On the 21st April 2009 an Arsenal player scored four goals against Liverpool. Who was he?

   a) Robin van Persie   b) Theo Walcott   c) Andrey Arshavin

15. Edwin van der Sar set a world record for the number of minutes in league games without conceding a goal. How many minutes was it?

   a) 978 minutes   b) 1,217 minutes   c) 1,311 minutes

16. Which was the team that ended the run?

   a) Newcastle   b) Fulham   c) West Ham

17. Tottenham signed Jermain Defoe from Portsmouth in January 2009 for around £15.75m. How much did Tottenham sell him to Portsmouth for in January 2008?

   a) £7.5m   b) £17.5m   c) £27.5m

18. By winning the league title this year Man Utd drew level with Liverpool with the most First Division and Premier League titles won. How many was it?

   a) 16   b) 18   c) 20

19. How many managers did Newcastle have this season before being relegated?

   a) 3   b) 4   c) 5

20. Who was the 18 year old who made his debut for Sunderland on the 1st November 2008 in a 5 – 0 defeat at Chelsea?

   a) Anton Ferdinand   b) Jordan Henderson   c) Jordan Pickford

Quiz 18: 2009 – 10 Season

1. **Chelsea won the league and scored a then Premier League record number of goals. How many did they get?**

   a) 99   b) 101   c) 103

2. **Chelsea won the league by one point with an 8 – 0 over which team in their final game?**

   a) Wigan   b) Fulham   c) Hull

3. **Who was the Chelsea manager for this season?**

   a) Andre Villas-Boas   b) Guus Hiddink   c) Carlo Ancelotti

4. **In February 2010 which team became the first to go into administration while in the Premier League?**

   a) Hull   b) Portsmouth   c) Wigan

5. **Only one of the promoted teams this season went straight back down. Which one?**

   a) Burnley   b) Wolves   c) Birmingham

6. **The quickest hat trick of the season was scored by Tottenham against Wigan in November 2009. Which Tottenham player took 6 minutes to get the three goals?**

   a) Luka Modric   b) Peter Crouch   c) Jermain Defoe

7. **Who won the golden boot in the 2009 – 10 season?**

   a) Carlos Tevez   b) Darren Bent   c) Didier Drogba

8. **Man Utd got 86 goals this season. How many were own goals?**

   a) 6   b) 8   c) 10

9. **Who was the Premier League Manager of the Season?**

   a) Harry Redknapp   b) Sir Alex Ferguson   c) Carlo Ancelotti

10. **On the 27th July Tottenham signed a player for £9m who had been an apprentice at the club before they let him go. Who was the player?**

   a) David Bentley   b) Jermaine Jenas   c) Peter Crouch

11. **On the 17th October 2009 one of the most notorious goals in Premier League history was scored when the football deflected off a beach ball that was on the pitch. Who scored the goal?**

   a) Jermain Defoe   b) Darren Bent   c) Louis Saha

12. **Which team were the victims of the 'beach ball goal'?**

   a) Everton   b) Liverpool   c) Chelsea

13. **Which team lost in the 2010 Europa League final?**

   a) Arsenal   b) Fulham   c) West Ham

14. **Which team, which avoided relegation, had the worst goal difference in the league?**

   a) Wigan   b) West Ham   c) Wolves

15. On the 19th December 2009 Man City sacked their manager. Who was he?

   a) Mark Hughes   b) Roberto Mancini   c) Roberto Matinez

16. Joe Hart spent the 2009 – 10 season playing for which club?

   a) Fulham   b) West Ham   c) Birmingham

17. On the 1st July 2009 Cristiano completed his move from Man Utd to Real Madrid. How much did Man Utd receive from Real Madrid?

   a) £80m   b) £100m   c) £120m

18. The Manchester derby on the 20th September 2009 at Old Trafford ends 4 – 3 to United. Who scored the stoppage time winner?

   a) Wayne Rooney   b) Paul Scholes   c) Michael Owen

19. Who did Burnley beat in their first top-flight game for 33 years on the 19th August 2009?

   a) Liverpool   b) Man Utd   c) Arsenal

20. The Burnley manager Owen Coyle left Burnley in January 2010 to join which club?

   a) West Ham   b) Fulham   c) Bolton

Quiz 19: 2010 – 11 Season

1. **Who won the title in 2010 – 11?**

   a) Man Utd   b) Arsenal   c) Chelsea

2. **There was a new Premier League rule this year that required clubs to have at least how many home grown players in their squad?**

   a) 6   b) 8   c) 10

3. **There was also a rule on how many players they could have in a squad. How many players were they allowed?**

   a) 22   b) 25   c) 28

4. **Blackpool played their first season in the Premier League this season. Who was their manager?**

   a) Owen Coyle   b) Tony Pulis   c) Ian Holloway

5. **Birmingham, despite being relegated, won a place in the Europa League for 2011 – 12. Why did they qualify?**

   a) They won the fair play league   b) They won the League Cup
   c) They were finalists in the FA Cup

6. **A Manchester United player got three hat tricks this season. Who was he?**

   a) Dimitar Berbatov   b) Wayne Rooney   c) Javier Hernandez

7. **Who was the Premier League Player of the Season for 2010 – 11?**

   a) Carlos Tevez   b) Gareth Bale   c) Nemanja Vidic

8. **Who won the Premier League Golden Glove for the most clean sheets in 2010 – 11?**

   a) Edwin van der Sar   b) Joe Hart   c) David James

9. **Who became manager of Liverpool on the 1st July 2010?**

   a) Roy Hodgson   b) Kenny Dalglish   c) Rafa Benitez

10. **Man City sign David Silva from Valencia in July 2010. How much did they pay in transfer fee?**

    a) £24m   b) £44m   c) £64m

11. **In January 2011 Chelsea pay a British record of £50m for which player?**

    a) David Luiz   b) Ramires   c) Fernando Torres

12. **On the 2nd February 2011 who announced their retirement from playing football after almost 20 years at Man Utd?**

    a) Gary Neville   b) Paul Scholes   c) Ryan Giggs

13. **On the 5th February 2011, a team set a record at Newcastle by losing a 4 – 0 lead they had gained after 26 minutes and conceded 4 goals in the 2nd half. Which team was this?**

    a) Liverpool   b) Chelsea   c) Arsenal

14. On the 6th March 2011, a Liverpool player got a hat trick against Man Utd for the first time since 1990. Who was it?

   a) Andy Carroll   b) Maxi Rodriguez   c) Dirk Kuyt

15. On the 29th June 2011 Man Utd signed David de Gea for £16.8m from which club?

   a) Real Madrid   b) Atletico Madrid   c) Barcelona

16. Which club had the lowest crowd capacity in 2010 – 11?

   a) Blackpool   b) Fulham   c) Wigan

17. Who was the Sunderland captain this season?

   a) Lee Cattermole   b) Titus Bramble   c) Phil Bardsley

18. Peter Odemwingie was West Brom's leading goal scorer with 15 goals this season. What national team did he represent?

   a) Soviet Union   b) Nigeria   c) Uzbekistan

19. On the 12th August 2010 who did Man City sign from Inter Milan?

   a) Kolo Toure   b) Edin Dzeko   c) Mario Balotelli

20. Who did Liverpool sign from Sunderland in June 2011 for £16m?

   a) Jordan Henderson   b) David N'Gog   c) Raul Meireles

Quiz 20: 2011 – 12 Season

— ✍ —

1. **Man City won the title this season. When was the last time they won it?**

   a) 1961   b) 1968   c) 1971

2. **Man City won the title on goal difference from Man Utd as they were both on 89 points. How much better was Man City's goal difference?**

   a) 4 goals   b) 6 goals   c) 8 goals

3. **Man City's goal difference was helped by a 6 – 1 away win against which team?**

   a) Fulham   b) Stoke   c) Man Utd

4. **Who scored the last goal of the season?**

   a) Sergio Aguero   b) Demba Ba   c) Robin van Persie

5. **QPR, Norwich and Swansea were promoted this season into the Premier League. How many were relegated this season?**

   a) 0   b) 2   c) 3

6. **Which Premier League team played at the Britannia Stadium this season?**

   a) Bolton   b) Wigan   c) Stoke

7. **Who was QPR's captain in 2011 -12?**

   a) Anton Ferdinand   b) Joey Barton   c) Jamie Mackie

8. **Who were Blackburn's shirt sponsor this season?**

   a) The Prince's Trust   b) Chang Beer   c) Wonga.com

9. **Who did Chelsea sack as manager on the 4th March 2012?**

   a) Roberto Di Matteo   b) Carlo Ancelotti   c) Andre Villas-Boas

10. **What position were Chelsea in the league when he was sacked?**

    a) 5th b) 10th c) 15th

11. **The fastest goal of the season was scored in 24 seconds by Andrea Orlandi for Swansea against Wolves. What nationality is he?**

    a) Croatian   b) Slovenian   c) Spanish

12. **Who won the Golden Boot in 2011 – 12?**

    a) Wayne Rooney   b) Robin van Persie   c) Sergio Aguero

13. **An American was Fulham's leading goal scorer with 17 goals in 2011 – 12. Who was he?**

    a) Clint Dempsey   b) Marcus Hahnemann   c) Brian McBride

14. **Which club had the most red cards with a total of 9 in 2011 – 12?**

    a) Blackburn   b) Man City   c) QPR

15. An Englishman was the Premier League Manager of the season, only the second after Harry Redknapp. Who was he?

   a) Roy Hodgson   b) Alan Pardew   c) Steve Bruce

16. Tottenham's opening league game on the 13th August 2011 against Everton was postponed. Why was it postponed?

   a) Structural problem with a stand   b) Rioting in the Tottenham area   c) Water leak flooded the ground

17. On the 8th February 2012 Harry Redknapp was cleared of charges at Southwark Crown Court. What was he charged with?

   a) Running over his wife   b) Not having a TV license   c) Tax evasion

18. Which former England player retired on the 2nd May 2012?

   a) David Beckham   b) Sol Campbell   c) Ashley Cole

19. On the 18th August 2011 Chelsea signed a player for £20m from Anderlecht. Who was he?

   a) Juan Mata   b) Nemanja Matic   c) Romelu Lukaku

20. Which club had the youngest average age in the Premier League in 2011 -12?

   a) Norwich   b) Manchester United   c) Arsenal

Quiz 21: 2012 – 13 Season

———— ∽◦ ————

1. **The club that won the FA Cup this season were also relegated. Which team was this?**

   a) QPR   b) Reading   c) Wigan

2. **Which Premier League team played at the Liberty Stadium this year?**

   a) Swansea   b) Reading   c) Bolton

3. **Who was the Arsenal captain in 2012 – 13?**

   a) Mikel Arteta   b) Per Mertesacker   c) Thomas Vermaelen

4. **In May 2013 Man City sacked which manager?**

   a) Roberto Mancini   b) Mark Hughes   c) Sven Goran-Eriksson

5. **In May 2013 two of Man Utd's 'Class of 92' retired. Which two was it?**

   a) Nicky Butt and Gary Neville   b) David Beckham and Paul Scholes   c) Ryan Giggs and Phil Neville

6. **The first goal of the season was scored by the Spanish footballer Michu. Who did he play for?**

   a) Fulham   b) QPR   c) Swansea

7. **Who was the Southampton captain in 2012 - 13?**

    a) Adam Lallana   b) Rickie Lambert   c) Morgan Schneiderlin

8. **Who won the Golden Boot in 2012 – 13?**

    a) Luis Suarez   b) Gareth Bale   c) Robin van Persie

9. **Luka Modric was signed in August 2012 by Spurs for £30m. Which club did they sign him from?**

    a) Real Madrid   b) Barcelona   c) Inter Milan

10. **In August 2012 Tottenham loaned out Harry Kane to which club?**

    a) Millwall   b) Norwich   c) Leicester

11. **Which goalkeeper won the Golden Glove by keeping 18 clean sheets during the season?**

    a) David de Gea   b) Pepe Reina   c) Joe Hart

12. **The 9th May 2013 was Alex Ferguson's final game in charge of Man Utd and was against West Brom. What was the score?**

    a) 3 – 3   b) 4 – 4   c) 5 -5

13. **On the 8th August 2012 who did Arsenal sign for £15m from Southampton?**

    a) Nicklas Bendtner   b) Alex Oxlade-Chamberlain   c) Theo Walcott

14. **Manchester United scored 83 goals in 2012 – 13. However they had a record number of goal scorers. How many individuals scored for Man Utd this season?**

    a) 18   b) 20   c) 22

15. Who was the only player in 2012 – 13 to play every single minute of every match?

   a) Pablo Zabaleta   b) Michael Carrick   c) Leighton Baines

16. On the 23rd November 2012 who was sacked as manager of Queens Park Rangers?

   a) Alex McLeish   b) Mark Hughes   c) Martin O'Neil

17. How many passes did Mikel Arteta complete this season?

   a) 1972   b) 2517   c) 3245

18. This was Alex Ferguson's final season in charge of Man Utd. How many times did he win the Premier League title?

   a) 9   b) 11   c) 13

19. How many penalties did Man Utd concede this season?

   a) 0   b) 1   c) 2

20. Who did Tottenham sign for £12m from Lyon in August 2012?

   a) Mousa Dembele   b) Hugo Lloris   c) Jan Vertonghen

Quiz 22: 2013 – 14 Season

———— ✐ ————

1. **Man Utd under David Moyes finished outside the top four for the first time in Premier League history. Where did they finish?**

   a) Fifth   b) Seventh   c) Ninth

2. **Which team were bottom of the league at Christmas but still avoided relegation?**

   a) Norwich   b) Fulham   c) Sunderland

3. **The fastest goal of the season was scored in 13 seconds by which player?**

   a) Asmir Begovic   b) Luis Suarez   c) Romelu Lukaku

4. **Who were Newcastle's shirt sponsor this season?**

   a) Bet365   b) Wonga   c) Loanpig.com

5. **Two teams scored over 100 goals for the first time in a Premier League season. One was the champions Man City, but who were the other team?**

   a) Chelsea   b) Tottenham   c) Liverpool

6. **Who won the golden boot in the 2013 – 14 season?**

   a) Sergio Aguero   b) Edin Dzeko   c) Luis Suarez

7. **In August 2013 Chelsea controversially signed Willian for £30m. He had already had a medical with which club who thought they had agreed his signing?**

   a) Arsenal   b) Tottenham   c) Man Utd

8. **Who was the Premier League Manager of the Season?**

   a) Manuel Pellegrini   b) Brendan Rogers   c) Tony Pulis

9. **What nationality is Manuel Pellegrini?**

   a) Chilean   b) Spanish   c) Italian

10. **In August 2013 Hull City owner Assem Allam created pandemonium amongst Hull fans by proposing a change of name of the club to help marketing in Asia. What was the proposed name?**

    a) Hull City Ninjas   b) Hull City Tigers   c) Hull City Heroes

11. **Which player got the most yellow cards during the season?**

    a) Pablo Zabaleta   b) Ryan Shawcross   c) Jan Vertonghen

12. **Man City needed a win in the last game of the season to guarantee they won the title, and they won 2 – 0. Who did they beat?**

    a) Everton   b) Fulham   c) West Ham

13. **On the 19th May 2014 Ryan Giggs retired after a long career with Man Utd. How many games did he play for them?**

    a) 852   b) 879   c) 963

14. On the 22nd March 2014 Arsenal played Chelsea at Stamford Bridge for Arsene Wenger's 1,000th game in charge. All did not go to plan for Arsenal and they lost, but what was the score?

    a) 4 – 2   b) 5 – 3   c) 6 – 0

15. In this game another bizarre incident occurred. What was it?

    a) A Chelsea goal was deflected off the referee   b) The referee sent the wrong person off   c) The game went on for 5 minutes too long when the referee's watch stopped

16. Which Everton player made the PFA Team of the Year?

    a) Seamus Coleman   b) Gareth Barry   c) Phil Jagielka

17. In January 2014 who did Man Utd sign from Chelsea?

    a) Jesse Lingard   b) Juan Mata   c) Marcos Rojo

18. On the same day Chelsea signed a midfielder from FC Basle. Who was he?

    a) Willian   b) Nemanja Matic   c) Mohamed Salah

19. Who was Newcastle's goalkeeper in 2013 – 14?

    a) Rob Elliot   b) Tim Krull   c) Tim Howard

20. David Moyes was sacked as Man Utd manager on 22nd April 2014. He was manager for a total of 51 games. How many did he win?

    a) 18   b) 23   c) 27

Quiz 23: 2014 – 15 Season

1. **Who won the title in the 2014 – 15 season?**

   a) Chelsea   b) Man City   c) Man Utd

2. **Which team played at the Liberty Stadium this season?**

   a) Southampton   b) Swansea   c) Stoke

3. **Who were Man Utd's shirt sponsor in 2014 – 15?**

   a) AIG   b) Chevrolet   c) Sharp

4. **Who was sacked as Sunderland manager on the 16th March 2015?**

   a) Paolo Di Canio   b) Dick Advocaat   c) Gus Poyet

5. **Which player won the Golden Boot in 2014 -15?**

   a) Harry Kane   b) Serio Aguero   c) Diego Costa

6. **In August 2014 who did Liverpool sign for £18m?**

   a) Adam Lallana   b) Dejan Lovren   c) Mario Balotelli

7. **Who was the Southampton player who was selected in the PFA Team of the Year?**

   a) Ryan Bertrand   b) Victor Wanyama   c) Toby Alderweireld

8. **Liverpool lost their last game of the season 6 -1. Which team beat them?**

   a) Man City   b) Arsenal   c) Stoke

9. **Who scored Liverpool's goal in their final game for the club?**

   a) Raheem Sterling   b) Steven Gerrard   c) Philippe Coutinho

10. **Which Southampton player scored the fastest ever Premier League hat trick in 2 minutes 56 seconds?**

    a) Victor Wayama   b) Shane Long   c) Sadio Mane

11. **On the 24th May 2015 Brad Friedel the former Liverpool, Tottenham, Blackburn and Aston Villa goalkeeper announced his retirement after 16 seasons in the Premier League. How many Premier League games did he play?**

    a) 461   b) 491   c) 531

12. **Which club received 92 yellow cards during the 2014 – 15 season?**

    a) Burnley   b) Aston Villa   c) Sunderland

13. **One player managed to get 14 yellow cards in the 27 Premier League games he played this season. Who was this?**

    a) Paul Konchesky   b) Tom Huddlestone   c) Lee Catermole

14. **Which player got 5 yellow cards for dissent in 2014 – 15?**

    a) Moussa Sissoko   b) Mark Noble   c) Diego Costa

15. Which player played every minute of the 2014 – 15 season?

a) Philippe Coutinho   b) Alexis Sanchez   c) John Terry

16. Which team achieved 17 draws out of 38 games this season?

a) Sunderland   b) Stoke   c) Aston Villa

17. Frank Lampard scored against his 39th Premier League opponents this season. Who were the victims?

a) Swansea   b) West Brom   c) Chelsea

18. How many days were Chelsea leading the Premier League during the 2014 – 15 season?

a) 14 days   b) 19 days   c) 274 days

19. Who had the most assists this season?

a) Cesc Fabregas   b) Santi Carzola   c) Angel Di Maria

20. What nationality is Angel Di Maria?

a) Chilean   b) Uruguayan   c) Argentinian

Quiz 24: 2015 – 16 Season

1. Leicester City won the Premier League title against the odds. What were the odds being offered by the bookies before the season started?

500 – 1   b) 5,000 – 1   c) 50,000 – 1

2. **Claudio Ranieri was the Leicester manager who took over in July 2015 and led them to glory but who was the Leicester manager who was sacked on the 30th June 2015?**

   a) Garry Monk   b) Tim Sherwood   c) Nigel Pearson

3. **Ranieri's previous job was as manager of Greece in which he lasted just 4 games. Who did they lose to in his last game?**

   a) Faroe Islands   b) Gibraltar   c) Vatican City

4. **Jamie Vardy scored in 11 consecutive Premier League games for Leicester to set a record. Whose record did he beat?**

   a) Thierry Henry   b) Ruud van Nistelrooy   c) Alan Shearer

5. **Which team did his run peter out against?**

   a)   Swansea   b) Liverpool   c) Man City

6. **Sam Allardyce became manager of a Premier League team on the 9th October 2015. They were 19th when he took over with three points from eight games, but he steered them away from relegation. Which team was it?**

   a) Sunderland   b) West Ham   c) Newcastle

7. **In August 2015 Manchester City signed Kevin De Bruyne. Which club did they sign him from?**

   a) Wolfsburg   b) Werder Bremen   c) Genk

8. **What nationality is Kevin De Bruyne?**

   a) French   b) Belgian   c) German

9. **On the 17th December 2015 Chelsea parted company with Jose Mourinho. How many of their 16 Premier League games had they won at this point in the season?**

   a) 4   b) 6   c) 8

10. **On the 28th August 2015 Tottenham signed Heung-min Son from which club?**

    a) Chelsea   b) Hamburg   c) Bayer Leverkusen

11. **Which player was sent off three times this season?**

    a) Lee Cattermole   b) Victor Wanyama   c) John Terry

12. **Aston Villa played over 3,500 minutes this season. How many of those minutes were they leading the match?**

    a) 243 minutes   b) 453 minutes   c) 785 minutes

13. **In February 2016 Louis Van Gaal famously dived on the touchline impersonating the opposition tactics. Who were the opposition?**

    a) Man City   b) Chelsea   c) Arsenal

14. **On the 23rd January 2016 Jurgen Klopp famously broke his glasses in celebrating a goal against Norwich. Who scored the goal?**

    a) James Milner   b) Christian Benteke   c) Adam Lallana

15. **Aston Villa beat Bournemouth 1 – 0 in their opening game. How many games did they play before they got another victory?**

    a) 15   b) 17   c) 19

16. **Which player scored 5 goals in a 6 – 1 win over Newcastle?**

   a) Alexis Sanchez   b) Harry Kane   c) Sergio Aguero

17. **How many points did Leicester win the title by?**

   a) 4 points   b) 7 points   c) 10 points

18. **Who came second in the league?**

   a) Arsenal   b) Man City   c) Tottenham

19. **Which player lost all 16 games that he participated in?**

   a) Micah Richards   b) Jack Grealish   c) Joleon Lescott

20. **The last round of games was scheduled for May 15th 2016. However, the Man Utd v Bournemouth game was played on the May 17th. Why was this?**

   a) Subsidence under a stand   b) A drone was flying overhead
   c) Bomb scare

Quiz 25: 2016 – 17 Season

1. **Leicester were the defending Premier League champions and managed the worst defense of a title. In what position did they finish the 2016 – 17 Premier League season?**

   a) 8th   b) 10th   c) 12th

2. **Burnley, Middlesbrough and Hull were the three promoted teams this season. Which was the only one to avoid relegation back to the Championship?**

   a) Burnley   b) Middlesbrough   c) Hull

3. **From the start of the 2016 – 17 season ticket prices for away fans was capped at how much?**

   a) £30   b) £40   c) £50

4. **Which team won the Premier League in 2016 – 17?**

   a) Man City   b) Chelsea   c) Man Utd

5. **Which team scored the most goals and conceded the least in the 2016 – 17 season?**

   a) Liverpool   b) Tottenham   c) Arsenal

6. **Which team finished 6th despite an unbeaten run of 25 games during the season?**

   a) Everton   b) Southampton   c) Man Utd

7. **Man Utd won the Europa League to be only the second English team to have won all three European trophies – European Cup/Champions League, Cup Winners Cup and UEFA Cup/UEFA Europa League. Which was the other team?**

   a) Liverpool   b) Chelsea   c) Aston Villa

8. **On the 23rd February 2017, despite the miracle of the previous season, Claudio Ranieri was sacked. Who replaced him?**

   a) Craig Shakespeare   b) Marco Silva   c) Paul Clement

9. **Bob Bradley was the first American manager to be appointed as the manager of a Premier League team. Which club appointed him?**

   a) Hull   b) Swansea   c) Crystal Palace

10. **Harry Kane won the Golden Boot with 29 goals. Who finished second with 25 goals?**

   a) Romelu Lukaku   b) Alexis Sanchez   c) Sergio Aguero

11. **How many hat tricks did Harry Kane get in 2016 – 17?**

   a) 2   b) 3   c) 4

12. **Harry Kane also scored more goals this season than which Premier League club?**

   a) Hull   b) Middlesbrough   c) Swansea

13. **On the 8th August 2016 Man Utd signed Paul Pogba for about £90m from which club?**

   a) Juventus   b) Lazio   c) Inter Milan

14. **Who won the Manager of the Month award in August 2016 but was sacked in January 2017?**

   a) Claudio Ranieri   b) Alan Pardew   c) Mike Phelan

15. **Salomon Rondon scored a hat trick against Swansea in December 2016. Why was it unusual?**

   a) They were all deflections from free kicks   b) It was scored in the first 10 minutes   c) They were all headers

16. **Teams were allowed 3 substitutes in a game this season. Which club used all 3 in every game?**

   a) Man Utd   b) Chelsea   c) Man City

17. Burnley won one away game all season. Who were the victims?

 a) Crystal Palace   b) Hull   c) Man Utd

18. On the 23rd December Chelsea sold Oscar to which Chinese club?

 a) Beijing Guoan   b) Shanghai SIPG   c) Jiangsu Suning

19. It was Tottenham's last season at White Hart Lane. Who scored Tottenham's last goal there?

 a) Harry Kane   b) Christian Eriksen   c) Dele Ali

20. On the 1st July 2016 Crystal Palace bought Andros Townsend from which club?

 a) Tottenham   b) QPR   c) Newcastle

Quiz 26: 2017 – 18 Season

1. Man City won the Premier league 2017 – 18 by a record points margin up till then. How many points did they win by?

 a) 17   b) 19   c) 21

2. Which team came second?

 a) Man Utd   b) Chelsea   c) Tottenham

3. **For the first time the Premier League allowed shirt sleeve sponsors. Who were Chelsea's shirt sleeve sponsors?**

   a) Angry Birds   b) Virgin Media   c) Alliance Tyres

4. **Huddersfield's manager was David Wagner. What nationality was he?**

   a) Scottish   b) American   c) Australian

5. **Which team's manager was Manager of the Month in April even though his team was relegated?**

   a) West Brom   b) Swansea   c) Stoke

6. **Which club had the smallest average attendance at home games?**

   a) Swansea   b) Watford   c) Bournemouth

7. **Despite winning the league convincingly Man City lost in the last 16 of the FA Cup to which League 1 team?**

   a) Scunthorpe   b) Wigan   c) Blackpool

8. **Frank de Boer was appointed Crystal Palace manager on the 26th June 2017. How many games did he last?**

   a) 4 games   b) 8 games   c) 12 games

9. **Mohamed Salah won the Golden Boot with 32 goals. How many teams did he not score against this season?**

   a) 1   b) 3   c) 5

10. **Alan Pardew was appointed manager of West Brom on the 29th November 2017 and sacked on 2nd April 2018. How many of his 21 games in charge did he win?**

   a) 1   b) 2   c) 3

11. **Sean Dyche said 'I'm very proud, I'm super proud, I'm the proudest man in Proudsville'. Who had they just beaten?**

a) Stoke   b) West Brom   c) Crystal Palace

12. **On the 27th December 2017 Liverpool signed Virgil van Dijk from Southampton. How much did they pay Southampton for him?**

a) £55m   b) £75m   c) 95m

13. **In July 2017 Liverpool signed Mohamed Salah from which club?**

a) Roma   b) Juventus   c) Inter Milan

14. **Crystal Place didn't score a Premier League goal in this season till October 17th. Who scored for them?**

a) Christian Benteke   b) Wilfred Zaha   c) Cesar Azpilicueta (OG)

15. **Zlatan Ibrahimović left Man Utd in March. How many goals did he score for Man Utd?**

a) 15   b) 17   c) 19

16. **In December 2017 Wayne Rooney scored from his own half for Everton. Who were the opponents?**

a) West Ham   b) Bournemouth   c) Crystal Palace

17. **On the 22nd January 2018 Alexis Sanchez joined Man Utd. What nationality is Sanchez?**

a) Peruvian   b) Chilean   c) Ecuadorian

18. Arsene Wenger's last home game in charge of Arsenal was against Burnley. What was the score?

   a) 5 – 0   b) 4 – 1   c) 3 – 2

19. In January 2018 Arsenal bought Pierre – Emerick Aubameyang from which club?

   a) Bayern Munich   b) Monaco   c) Borussia Dortmund

20. In winning the Premier League Man City scored a record number of goals. How many did they score?

   a) 102 goals   b) 106 goals   c) 110 goals

Quiz 27: 2018 – 19 Season

1. Man City were the champions this season, but who finished second?

   a) Man Utd   b) Chelsea   c) Liverpool

2. Man City lost 4 games during the season. How many did the second placed team lose?

   a) 1   b) 2   c) 3

3. Which club had the highest attendance for a game in 2018 – 19?

   a) Man Utd   b) Tottenham   c) Arsenal

4. **On the 23rd April 2019 Shane Long of Southampton scored the quickest goal in Premier League history against Watford. How long did it take him?**

   a) 6.23 seconds   b) 7.69 seconds   c) 8.91 seconds

5. **On 19th July 2018 Liverpool signed Alisson, the most expensive goalkeeper of all time to that point. Who did they sign him from?**

   a) Inter Milan   b) Roma   c) Juventus

6. **What nationality is Alisson?**

   a) Spanish   b) Portuguese   c) Brazilian

7. **Man City lost one home game all season. Who did they lose to?**

   a) Crystal Palace   b) Arsenal   c) Chelsea

8. **The Golden Boot was shared by 3 players with 22 goals. Two were Mohamed Salah and Sadio Mane. Who was the other?**

   a) Sergio Aguero   b) Jamie Vardy   c) Pierre-Emerick Aubameyang

9. **Who was the only Tottenham player to get a hat trick in 2018 -19 in a 4 – 0 win over Huddersfield?**

   a) Harry Kane   b) Dele Ali   c) Lucas Moura

10. **What was Huddersfield's ground called?**

   a) Falmer Stadium   b) Kirklees Stadium   c) Dean Court

11. Only two English players made the PFA Team of the Year. One was Raheem Sterling but who was the other?

   a) Harry Kane   b) Jamie Vardy   c) Trent Alexander-Arnold

12. On the 18th December 2018 Man Utd sacked Mourinho and replaced him with Ole Gunnar Solksjaer till the end of the season as a caretaker. Which Norwegian club had they loaned him from as manager?

   a) Viking   b) Odd   c) Molde

13. On the 3rd January 2019, the last undefeated team in the top five divisions lost. Who were they?

   a) Man City   b) Chelsea   c) Liverpool

14. On the 24th February 2019 Man City won the Carabao Cup with victory over Chelsea. Which player refused to come off when subbed?

   a) David Luiz   b) Kepa Arrizabalaga   c) Callum Hudson-Odoi

15. On the 20th October 2018 who became the first player born in the 2000s to score a Premier League goal?

   a) Ryan Sessegnon   b) James Maddison   c) Phil Foden

16. Which team suffered the heaviest defeat of the season?

   a) Fulham   b) Huddersfield   c) Chelsea

17. There were four clubs who were top of the league during the season. Liverpool were for 141 days, Man City for 125

days and Chelsea for 9 days. Which team were top for 1 day?

a) Arsenal   b) Man Utd   c) Tottenham

18. **Huddersfield only won 3 games all season. Who did they beat twice?**

a) Tottenham   b) Wolves   c) Fulham

19. **Who were the only team not to have a player sent off all season?**

a) Man City   b) Arsenal   c) Chelsea

20. **Which player scored 3 own goals this season, which was more than any other player?**

a) Connor Coady   b) Phil Jones   c) David Kuiz

Quiz 28: 2019 – 20 Season

1. **On the 13th March 2020 it was decided to suspend the season due to the Covid-19 pandemic. How many points were Liverpool ahead in the league at that point?**

a) 18 points   b) 20 points   c) 22 points

2. **Which team had scored the most goals when the league was suspended?**

a) Liverpool   b) Man City   c) Leicester

3. **On the 25th October 2019 Southampton suffered the biggest home loss in Premier League history with a 0 – 9 drubbing. Who inflicted the defeat?**

   a) Arsenal   b) Leicester   c) Man City

4. **Liverpool had a run of 27 unbeaten matches, including 18 consecutive wins. They were beaten on the 29th February 2020 by which team?**

   a) Norwich   b) Aston Villa   c) Watford

5. **How many London based teams were in the Premier League in the 2019 – 20 season?**

   a) 5   b) 6   c) 7

6. **Who were Brighton's shirt sponsor in 2019 – 20?**

   a) Vitality   b) LoveBet   c) American Express

7. **Who was Burnley's captain in 2019 – 20?**

   a) Ben Mee   b) James Tarkowski   c) Charlie Taylor

8. **How many points did Liverpool win the Premier League by?**

   a) 15   b) 18   c) 21

9. **Who was the FWA Footballer of the Year?**

   a) Kevin De Bruyne   b) Marcus Rashford   c) Jordan Henderson

10. **Which team had the most yellow cards in 2019 – 20 in the Premier League?**

    a) Brighton   b) Watford   c) Arsenal

11. **Which goalkeeper won the Golden Glove for the most clean sheets?**

    a) Ederson   b) Alisson   c) Nick Pope

12. **Only one player scored more than one hat trick this season. Who was he?**

    a) Jaimie Vardy   b) Sergio Aguero   c) Raheem Sterling

13. **How old was Roy Hodgson this season?**

    a) 72   b) 73   c) 74

14. **Liverpool broke the record for the most games remaining when they mathematically won the title. How many remained?**

    a) 7   b) 8   c) 9

15. **How many teams in the Premier League this season have never been relegated from it?**

    a) 4   b) 6   c) 8

16. **How many times did Crystal Palace score more than 2 goals in a league game this season?**

    a) 0   b) 1   c) 2

17. **Which Premier League player was fouled the most times this season?**

    a) Richarlison   b) Sergio Aguero   c) Jack Grealish

18. **Man Utd won a record number of penalties for a Premier League season. How many did they get?**

    a) 14   b) 15   c) 16

19. Man City got the biggest home win of the season with an 8 – 0 thrashing of which club?

a) Watford   b) Norwich   c) Bournemouth

20. The three relegated teams, Norwich, Bournemouth and Watford were coincidentally all promoted together in which season?

a) 2013 – 14   b) 2015 – 16   c) 2017 - 18

Quiz 29: Miscellaneous 1

1. Which former Premier League club finished in the lowest position of all the former Premier League clubs at the end of the 2018 – 19 season?

a) Oldham   b) Coventry   c) Barnsley

2. In 2010 Chelsea thrashed Wigan 6 – 0 away at Wigan. What was unusual about the game?

a) There were six different scorers   b) Wigan scored three own goals   c) There were no corners

3. Alan Shearer has scored the most goals in Premier League history with 260 goals. Who is second on the list?

a) Wayne Rooney   b) Andy Cole   c) Thierry Henry

4. **Which manager has been promoted to the Premier League the most times?**

   a) Tony Pulis   b) Sam Allardyce   c) Steve Bruce

5. **Which goalkeeper has the most clean sheets in Premier League history?**

   a) David James   b) Petr Cech   c) Brad Friedel

6. **Who received the first red card in Premier League history?**

   a) Niall Quinn   b) Paul Scholes   c) Gary Neville

7. **Which was the first club to score 1,000 Premier League goals?**

   a) Arsenal   b) Man Utd   c) Man City

8. **Which of these goalkeepers has not scored a Premier League goal?**

   a) Paul Robinson   b) Neville Southall   c) Brad Friedel

9. **Paulo Wanchope played Premier League football for Derby, West Ham and Man City. What nationality is he?**

   a) Costa Rican   b) Nigerian   c) Belgian

10. **Which club did Stuart Pearce manage in 2005 – 07?**

    a) Notts Forest   b) Fulham   c) Man City

11. **Which Premier League club was originally called St. Domingo FC?**

    a) Arsenal   b) Crystal Palace   c) Everton

12. Who is the only player born before 1960 to have scored a hat trick in the Premier League?

a) Gordon Strachan   b) Teddy Sheringham   c) Les Ferdinand

13. Two players scored in each of the first 16 Premier League seasons (1992 – 93 to 2007 – 08). One was Ryan Giggs but who was the other?

a) Frank Lampard   b) Steven Gerrard   c) Gary Speed

14. Who was Man City's first overseas manager?

a) Manuel Pellegrini   b) Sven Goran Erikson   c) Roberto Mancini

15. In October 2005 what did Jose Mourinho call Arsene Wenger?

a) Voyeur   b) Idiot   c) Worzel

16. In the 1992 – 93 Norwich finished in their highest Premier League position which was third. What was unusual about this result?

a) They didn't win away from home   b) They had negative goal difference   c) They didn't draw any games

17. Which of the following teams was not in the inaugural Premier League in 1992 – 93?

a) Sheffield Wednesday   b) Newcastle   c) Oldham

18. In the 1992 – 93 season which London based club finished highest in the league?

a) Crystal Palace   b) Arsenal   c) QPR

19. In 1996 – 97 which of the following did not happen to Middlesbrough?

a) Lost in FA Cup Final   b) Lost in League Cup Final   c) Relegated

20. Who is the oldest manager to have taken charge of a Premier League club?

a) Sir Alex Ferguson   b) Roy Hodgson   c) Bobby Robson

Quiz 30: Miscellaneous 2

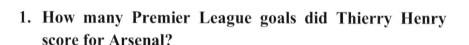

1. How many Premier League goals did Thierry Henry score for Arsenal?

a) 165 goals   b) 175 goals   c) 185 goals

2. On the 25th May 2006 Chelsea signed Andriy Shevchenko from AC Milan. What nationality is he?

a) Ukrainian   b) Russian   c) Bulgarian

3. Who is Aston Villa's oldest goal scorer in the Premier League?

a) Steve Stone   b) Gordon Cowans   c) Peter Schmeichel

4. Which club is 'dreaming dreams, scheming schemes and building castles high'?

a) West Ham   b) Fulham   c) Man Utd

5. **Which player scored his 150th Premier League goal while playing for Stoke?**

   a) Andy Cole   b) Teddy Sheringham   c) Michael Owen

6. **In their 'Invincible Season' of 2003 – 04 who did Arsenal come from behind to beat in their last game?**

   a) Charlton   b) Birmingham   c) Leicester

7. **Which team's logo includes the word 'Prepared' underneath a lion?**

   a) Aston Villa   b) Fulham   c) Watford

8. **In 1996 – 97 David Beckham famously scored from the halfway line. Who was the goalkeeper he beat?**

   a) Tim Flowers   b) Neil Sullivan   c) David Seaman

9. **Which player made 310 consecutive Premier League appearances between August 2004 and October 2010?**

   a) David James   b) Mark Schwarzer   c) Brad Friedel

10. **Who scored a hat trick for Charlton on their home Premiership debut?**

    a) Mark Kinsella   b) Clive Mendonca   c) Neil Redfearn

11. **How many non-British players participated on the opening day of the Premier League?**

    a) 6   b) 13   c) 18

12. **Who was the first Premier League manager to have received a Premier League winners medal from his playing days?**

    a) Gianluca Vialli   b) Bryan Robson   c) Graeme Souness

13. How many consecutive matches did Ole Gunnar Solksjaer win when appointed the Manchester United manager?

    a) 6   b) 8   c) 10

14. Which club did David Moyes manage before going to Everton?

    a) Bury   b) Preston   c) Oldham

15. In 2003 which Fulham player donned a Zorro mask after he had scored?

    a) Luis Boa Morte   b) Bryan Hayles   c) Facundo Sava

16. Kasey Keller and Neil Sullivan have both kept goal for which club?

    a) Tottenham   b) Leicester   c) Fulham

17. In April 2005 which Newcastle player was sent off for brawling with teammate Lee Bowyer?

    a) Kieron Dyer   b) Jonathan Woodgate   c) Keith Gillespie

18. Which ground of the teams that have played Premier League has been in the longest continuous use?

    a) Old Trafford   b) Turf Moor   c) Goodison

19. Who is the highest scoring foreign player in the Premier League?

    a) Robin van Persie   b) Jimmy Floyd Hasselbaink   c) Thierry Henry

20. Only one player has scored 5 goals in one half of a Premier League football game. Who is he?

a) Andy Cole   b) Jermaine Defoe   c) Alan Shearer

Answers

Quiz 1: 1992 – 93 Season Answers

1. Leeds United
2. 22
3. £304m
4. Ipswich
5. John Lyall
6. They beat Leicester City 1 – 0
7. It was Aston Villa
8. Man Utd got 84 points and Aston Villa 74 points. So 10 points was the margin of victory
9. It was Teddy Sheringham against Liverpool
10. It was Oldham with a capacity of 13,512. Southampton's was 15,200 and QPR's was 18,439
11. George Graham
12. Ian Porterfield
13. It was Eric Cantona on the 25th August 1992 for Leeds United against Tottenham
14. There were 13 – Schmeichel (Man Utd), Cantona (Leeds), Warzycha (Everton), Jensen (Arsenal), Limpar (Arsenal), Halle (Oldham), Rosenthal (Liverpool), Vonk (Man City), Kanchelskis (Man Utd), Forrest (Ipswich), Nilsson (Sheff Wed), Segers (Wimbledon) and Stejskal (QPR)
15. It was Notts Forest who finished bottom. Crystal Palace and Middlesbrough also went down with them.
16. Teddy Sheringham was the leading scorer with 22 goals
17. It was Paul McGrath. The Football Writers chose Chris Waddle and Ryan Giggs was the Young Player of the Year

18. It was Norwich who won 10 of their first 16 matches
19. He came from Everton
20. It was Les Ferdinand who scored 20 goals.

Quiz 2: 1993 – 94 Season Answers

1. It was Carling Breweries
2. It was Swindon
3. Graeme Souness
4. Man Utd
5. Newcastle scored 82 goals while Man Utd scored 80. Man Utd won the League by 15 points
6. Tim Flowers who was transferred from Southampton to Blackburn
7. Unfortunately, they conceded 100 goals
8. It was Bryan Robson who became the Middlesbrough player manager
9. They played at Crystal Palace's ground, Selhurst Park
10. It was the Argentinian Ossie Ardiles
11. It was Andy Cole who scored 34 goals for Newcastle
12. It was Robbie Fowler
13. It was Liverpool in 1985 -86
14. George Graham
15. The unlucky ones were Sheff Utd
16. Newcastle United
17. It was Everton who came back from 2 – 0 down after 20 minutes
18. It was Sir Matt Busby
19. The club was Tottenham though the points deduction was quashed after appeals
20. Eric Cantona

Quiz 3: 1994 -95 Season Answers

1. Chris Sutton

2. They scored 49 goals
3. It was West Ham
4. Notts Forest
5. It was 4 relegated, and with only 2 promoted allowed the Premier League to reduce to 20 teams
6. The victims were Ipswich
7. Andy Cole
8. It was Crystal Palace and Cantona was banned from football for 8 months
9. It was a taxi driver. He was given a 3 month sentence which was overturned on appeal
10. It was Southampton. The Dell could only hold 15,200 souls
11. It was Jurgen Klinsmann
12. It was bungs. It was revealed that he accepted £425,000 illegal payments from an agent for transfers
13. He left for Southampton
14. It was 19 year old Robbie Fowler
15. It was Dion Dublin
16. Gary Lineker
17. Joe Royle
18. Andy Cole for Man Utd against Ipswich
19. They lost 2 – 1 at Liverpool
20. They had previously won the First Division in 1913 – 14. This is 81 years prior

Quiz 4: 1995 – 96 Season Answers

1. It was Man Utd
2. Inter Milan
3. It was Robbie Fowler with 28 goals
4. He scored 5 hat tricks. They were against Coventry, Notts Forest, West Ham, Bolton and Tottenham
5. He was born in Ghana
6. It was Les Ferdinand
7. They led by 10 points from Man Utd

8. It was Man City
9. He was signed from Notts Forest
10. Alan Ball
11. It was David Platt
12. Dion Dublin scored three goals for Coventry against Sheffield Wednesday but still lost 4 – 3
13. It was Steve McManaman who had 15 assists
14. He played for Coventry
15. It was Frank Lampard. Rio Ferdinand made his debut for West Ham on the 5th May 1995
16. He won 20 trophies. They were 6 league titles, 3 league cups, 6 Charity Shields, 3 European Cups, 1 UEFA Cup and 1 UEFA Super Cup
17. He is Australian
18. His name is Jean-Marc Bosman
19. Steve Bruce
20. It was David James

Quiz 5: 1996 – 97 Season Answers

1. It was Newcastle
2. Fabrizio Ravanelli
3. Bruce Rioch
4. He managed Grampus Eight, a Japanese team
5. It was Roberto Di Matteo who they bought from Lazio
6. AC Milan
7. It was Wimbledon
8. It was Ian Wright who scored 23 goals for Arsenal
9. It was Gianfranco Zola. Shearer was the PFA Player of the Year and Juninho was the 'Premier League Player of the Year'
10. It was Kenny Dalglish
11. Eric Cantona
12. The reason was non fulfillment of fixtures. They postponed a fixture against Blackburn because too many players were ill or injured. The League took a dim view and docked them 3

points.

13. It was Ruud Gullit when he took Chelsea to the FA Cup
14. Kevin Keegan's Newcastle got the victory
15. It was Southampton
16. He resigned after 33 days citing the pressure of the job
17. It was Stan Collymore
18. It was Michael Owen. Jaimie Carragher made his debut earlier in the season
19. He was 40 years old
20. John Barnes

Quiz 6: 1997 – 98 Season Answers

1. Arsenal
2. David Pleat
3. They were all relegated
4. Dion Dublin
5. It was Gianluca Vialli
6. Paul Ince
7. Danny Murphy
8. It was Burnden Park
9. Tottenham
10. It was the USA goalkeeper Brad Friedel
11. Floodlights kept failing causing games to be abandoned. It was felt this happened when results were 'unfavourable'. Teams affected were West Ham, Derby, Arsenal and Bolton
12. It was Manchester City
13. Crystal Palace
14. It was David Beckham who made 13 assists. Bergkamp made 12 and Sheringham 10
15. It was Nigel Martyn of Leeds United
16. It was JVC
17. Bolton had a goal disallowed after it hit the crossbar and TV replays showed that it had crossed the line
18. It was Martin O'Neil

19. Colin Hendry (Blackburn)
20. Harry Redknapp

Quiz 7: 1998 – 99 Season Answers

1. They lost 3 league games all season
2. It was Derby
3. Kenny Dalglish
4. The unfortunate victims were Notts Forest
5. Of course, it was Ole Gunnar Solksjaer. He did it on the 6th February 1998 against Notts Forest. He ended up with four goals.
6. It was David Ginola
7. It was Arsenal and David Seaman was the goalkeeper
8. It was Nolberto Solano
9. He came from Aston Villa
10. Christian Gross
11. George Graham
12. The bid came from Rupert Murdoch's BSKYB, but was blocked by the Monopolies and Mergers Committee
13. Jermaine Pennant
14. Forest got a 1 – 0 win at Everton in their 20th league game of the season
15. It was Steven Gerrard in a win over Blackburn Rovers
16. Jimmy Floyd Hasselbaink
17. Jimmy Floyd Hasselbaink
18. It was Alan Curbishley
19. Dwight Yorke
20. The Tottenham player was David Ginola. The Arsenal players were Emmanuel Petit, Patrick Vieira and Nicolas Anelka

Quiz 8:1999 – 00 Season Answers

1. They won by 18points
2. Arsenal

3. They didn't win any away games
4. It was Wimbledon
5. Bobby Robson
6. Vasco da Gama
7. David O'Leary
8. Arsenal sold Nicolas Anelka
9. Arsenal invested £11m of the Anelka fee
10. It was Robbie Keane
11. Sheffield Wednesday
12. George Weah joined the Blues on loan
13. He was signed from Monaco
14. It was Kevin Phillips of Sunderland who got 30 goals
15. It was Danny Wilson. Four Sheffield MPs were calling for his sacking
16. Chelsea beat Aston Villa 1 – 0
17. It was Watford who finished with a record low of 24 points, which has since been beaten
18. Jaap Stam
19. Joe Royle
20. It was Valley Parade though is now known as the Utilita Energy Stadium for sponsorship reasons

Quiz 9: 2000 – 01 Season Answers

1. Ipswich Town
2. It was Gerard Houllier
3. Gianluca Vialli
4. It was Steven Gerrard
5. It was Marcus Stewart who got 18 goals for Ipswich this season
6. Southampton
7. It was Everton
8. They paid £18m to West Ham for Rio Ferdinand
9. It was Peter Crouch
10. Roy Keane

11. All three were relegated but Bradford were bottom
12. Mark Viduka got 4 goals for Leeds United in a 4 – 3 home win against Liverpool
13. It was George Burley of Ipswich who finished 5th in their first season back in the Premier League
14. It was Sylvinho of Arsenal
15. Teddy Sheringham
16. He was born in Costa Rica
17. They won on penalties and were the first English team to win a trophy by this method
18. It was Robbie Keane
19. Frank Lampard
20. There were 3 teams prior to Man Utd. They were Huddersfield Town (1923/4 to 1925/6), Arsenal (1932/3 to 1934/5) and Liverpool (1981/2 to 1983/84)

Quiz 10: 2001 – 02 Season Answers

1. It was Barclaycard
2. Wayne Bridge
3. They had done it twice before – 1970 – 71 and 1997 – 98
4. They achieved all three
5. It was Veron who was signed from Lazio
6. It was Leeds United
7. He was at Preston
8. It was Jerzy Dudek
9. Inter Milan
10. They won the Fair Play League
11. It was Roberto Di Matteo
12. Stewart Downing
13. Graham Taylor
14. It was Paul Merson
15. Thierry Henry was the leading goal scorer with 24 goals
16. It was Jermaine Jenas
17. Marcel Desailly

18. He was sold to Lazio after Fergie was unhappy about Stam's autobiography
19. The 'Battle of Bramall Lane' resulted in only 6 Sheffield players being on the pitch thanks to 3 players being sent off and injuries. As this fell below the minimum 7 players the referee abandoned the game.
20. It was Freddie Ljunberg of Arsenal

Quiz 11: 2002 – 03 Season Answers

1. It was Man Utd who beat them 2 – 0 at Old Trafford
2. They played at Loftus Road
3. Titus Bramble
4. Arsenal
5. It was Wayne Rooney for Everton against Arsenal. James Milner beat the record on Boxing Day 2002
6. It was Arsenal who won 2 – 0 at Old Trafford
7. The state of the pitch was the problem. They were going to relay the pitch after a game against Charlton. Prior to the game they removed the grass surface and played the game on the sandy base
8. Johnathan Woodgate
9. Terry Venables
10. They managed to get 21 goals
11. They got through 3 managers – Peter Reid and Howard Wilkinson were sacked before Mick McCarthy was appointed till the end of the season
12. They went down with 42 points
13. Carlsberg
14. Patrick Vieira
15. It was Ruud van Nistelrooy who scored 25 goals
16. Blackburn Rovers who had 15 clean sheets
17. Tony Adams
18. David Beckham was sold for £25m to Real Madrid after 12 years at Man Utd

19. It was called The Reebok Stadium
20. Southampton

Quiz 12: 2003 – 04 Season Answers

1. They finished with 12 draws
2. It was Preston in the league's first season in 1888 – 89 in a 22 game season
3. Chelsea
4. It was Adrian Mutu, who was banned for failing a drugs test for cocaine use
5. It was Steve McClaren, who's Middlesbrough won the League Cup
6. It was Portsmouth
7. Glenn Hoddle
8. Scott Parker
9. It was the Bolton manager Sam Allardyce in November and January
10. It was Tim Howard who was signed from an American team MetroStars
11. It was missed drugs tests
12. Jermain Defoe
13. It was Feyenoord
14. Rafa Benitez
15. Claudio Ranieri
16. Man Utd beat them 1 – 0 at Villa Park
17. David Seaman
18. It was Thierry Henry who scored 30 goals
19. He is Argentinian
20. It was 6 players – Lauren, Ashley Cole, Sol Campbell, Patrick Vieira, Robert Pires and Thierry Henry

Quiz 13: 2004 – 05 Season Answers

1. They got 95 points

2. He left after 13 games
3. It was West Brom who had been 8 points from safety on Christmas Day
4. Man Utd beat Arsenal 2 – 0 at Old Trafford
5. It was Northern Rock
6. Stuart Pearce
7. £27m
8. Sir Bobby Robson
9. It was Kieron Dyer
10. AC Milan
11. Ledley King
12. Southampton
13. The conceded a record of only 15 goals
14. It was Ray Parlour who was playing for Middlesbrough
15. Senegal
16. They got 15 away wins
17. They lost 1 – 0 to Man City
18. It was Thierry Henry who scored 25 goals
19. Petr Cech won it with 25 clean sheets including 10 consecutively
20. Arsenal won it for the second year running with Tottenham second. Blackburn were the worst in the league

Quiz 14: 2005 – 06 Season Answers

1. They were elected in 1978. Boston had finished above them, but their ground didn't meet the qualifying standard
2. It was Chelsea who retained the title from the previous season
3. Their only home victory in this season was against Fulham which they won 2 – 1
4. Reading
5. FC United of Manchester joined the North West Counties League Division 2
6. Arran Lennon
7. Patrick Vieira was sold to Juventus

8. They beat CSKA Moscow 3 – 1
9. They scored their 1,000[th] Premier League goal. It was a header by Ronaldo in a 4 – 1 defeat by Middlesbrough
10. Theo Walcott
11. Surprisingly it was 1921
12. Charlton
13. Thierry Henry
14. It was Martin Jol
15. Pascal Chimbonda
16. It was Pepe Reina who kept 20 Premier League clean sheets for Liverpool
17. Wigan moved from Springfield Park in 1999 to the JJB Stadium. It was renamed in 2009 after chairman David Whelan
18. Man Utd beat them 1 – 0 at Old Trafford
19. It was Wigan who they beat 4 – 2 thanks to a Thierry Henry hat trick
20. Yes Sunderland beat their own low of the 2002 – 03 when they got 19 points

Quiz 15: 2006 – 07 Season Answers

1. Dimitar Berbatov because he played for Spurs during this season
2. It was the 500,000[th]
3. It was Reading
4. It was Reading again who finished 8th
5. AIG
6. Charlton
7. Ecuador
8. 380 games
9. Gareth Barry
10. It was Chelsea who only had 3 losses. The champions were Man Utd who had 5 losses. Chelsea also had 11 draws.
11. It was Didier Drogba with 20 goals

12. It was Paul Robinson with an 83 yard free kick for Spurs against Watford. Peter Schmeichel scored one in 2001 and Brad Friedel in 2004

13. It was Carlos Tevez. He was ineligible because he was not owned by West Ham but by a third party. After various legal arguments West Ham paid compensation to Sheffield United

14. Real Madrid

15. 15,000th goal

16. It was Stuart Pearce

17. Man Utd

18. It was Pepe Reina who kept 19 clean sheets and won the award for a second season. Tim Howard kept 14 clean sheets and Marcus Hahnemann 13.

19. He is American

20. Reading

Quiz 16: 2007 – 08 Season

1. It was only the one. A 1 - 0 win at home against Newcastle

2. The 2 – 0 victory came at Wigan

3. Chelsea

4. It was Marcus Bent

5. Emmanuel Adebayor

6. It was David James

7. He is Norwegian

8. It was Avram Grant

9. Kevin Keegan for a second spell in the job

10. It was Roy Keane so the answer is Irish

11. Chelsea

12. Dinamo Zagreb

13. Steve Bruce

14. It was Man City

15. Cristiano Ronaldo

16. It was Wigan with an average home attendance of 19,046

17. West Ham

18. There were 61 red cards
19. Cesc Fabregas had 19 assists, Ashley Young had 17 and Wayne Rooney 13
20. Roy Hodgson

Quiz 17: 2008 – 09 Season Answers

1. Teams were allowed 7 substitutes, an increase from 5
2. It was Liverpool who beat them 2 – 1 at Anfield and 4 – 1 at Old Trafford
3. Russia
4. It was Tottenham
5. West Brom
6. It was Gabriel Agbonlahor
7. Nicolas Anelka
8. Gianfranco Zola
9. It was Robinho from Real Madrid. Kompany and Zabaleta were signed in the previous fortnight
10. David James
11. Harry Redknapp
12. It was the league runners up Liverpool with 2 losses. Man Utd had 4 losses and Chelsea 5
13. He played for Aston Villa and scored the goal against Everton
14. Andrey Arshavin
15. It was 1,311 minutes
16. Peter Lovenkrands of Newcastle scored after 9 minutes of their game on the 4th March 2009
17. It was £7.5m
18. They had both won 18 titles
19. They got through 4 managers – Kevin Keegan, Joe Kinnear, Chris Hughton and Alan Shearer. Joe Kinnear was incapacitated with heart problems
20. Jordan Henderson

Quiz 18: 2009 – 10 Season Answers

1. They scored 103 goals
2. They beat Wigan
3. Carlo Ancelotti
4. It was Portsmouth who were docked 9 points
5. Burnley
6. It was Jermain Defoe
7. Didier Drogba
8. Surprisingly, the opposition contributed 10 goals to Man Utd's total
9. It was Harry Redknapp
10. Peter Crouch
11. It was Darren Bent
12. Liverpool were the victims with Sunderland getting a 1 – 0 win at the Stadium of Light
13. Fulham lost 2 – 1 in extra time to Atletico Madrid
14. It was Wigan with a goal difference of – 41 goals. They lost 9 -1 to Tottenham and 8 – 0 to Chelsea which didn't help
15. Mark Hughes
16. Man City loaned him out to Birmingham
17. £80m
18. Michael Owen
19. They beat defending champions Man Utd 1 – 0
20. It was Bolton

Quiz 19: 2010 – 11 Season Answers

1. Man Utd
2. It was 8
3. They were allowed 25
4. Ian Holloway
5. They won the League Cup
6. It was Dimitar Berbatov against Liverpool, Blackburn and Birmingham

7. Nemanja Vidic
8. Joe Hart won it with 18 clean sheets for Man City
9. It was Roy Hodgson who replaced Rafa Benitez
10. £24m
11. Fernando Torres
12. Gary Neville
13. It was Arsenal
14. Dirk Kuyt
15. Atletico Madrid
16. Blackpool's capacity was 16,220, Fulham's 25,700 and Wigan's 25,133
17. Lee Cattermole
18. He was born in Tashkent, which was then part of the Soviet Union but is now part of Uzbekistan. He represented Nigeria though
19. Mario Balotelli
20. Jordan Henderson

Quiz 20: 2011 – 12 Season Answers

1. 1971
2. Man City's goal difference was 8 better than United's
3. Man Utd. If United had lost 2 – 1 they would have been champions
4. Sergio Aguero with the goal that won the title for Man City in the 4th minute of stoppage time
5. None were relegated for the first time since 2001 – 02
6. Stoke City. The name was changed in 2016 to the bet365 Stadium
7. Joey Barton
8. It was the Prince's Trust
9. Andre Villas-Boas
10. There were 5th
11. He is Spanish
12. Robin van Persie scored 30 goals, Wayne Rooney 27 goals

and Sergio Aguero 23 goals

13. Clint Dempsey
14. It was QPR with Joey Barton and Djibril Cisse leading the way with 2 each
15. It was the Newcastle manager Alan Pardew
16. There was rioting in the Tottenham area
17. It was tax evasion
18. Sol Campbell
19. It was Romelu Lukaku
20. The average age of the Norwich squad was 25.08 years, Man Utd 25.31 years and Arsenal 25.33 years

Quiz 21: 2012 – 13 Season Answers

1. It was Wigan won the FA Cup beating Man City 1 - 0
2. Swansea
3. Thomas Vermaelen
4. It was Roberto Mancini. They were second in the league at the time
5. It was David Beckham and Paul Scholes
6. He played for Swansea
7. Adam Lallana
8. It was Robin van Persie with 26 goals
9. Real Madrid
10. He was loaned out to all three but for 2012 – 13 it was Norwich City
11. Joe Hart
12. The score was 5 -5
13. Alex Oxlade - Chamberlain
14. There were 20 separate goal scorers
15. It was Leighton Baines
16. It was Mark Hughes. McLeish was sacked by Aston Villa and O'Neill by Sunderland this season
17. It was a total of 2517 passes, which is an average of 74 in the 34 games he played.

18. He won the title a total of 13 times
19. None
20. Hugo Lloris

Quiz 22: 2013 – 14 Season Answers

1. They finished seventh
2. It was Sunderland who finished 14th
3. Surprisingly it was the goalkeeper Asmir Begovic for Stoke against Southampton. The distance was measured as 97.5 yards and was, according to the 2015 Guinness Book of Records, the longest goal scored in football.
4. Wonga
5. Liverpool who scored 101 goals. Man City got 102 goals
6. It was Luis Suarez who scored 31 goals
7. It was Tottenham who were left waiting at the altar
8. Tony Pulis won the award for steering Crystal Palace to 11th place after losing 9 of their first ten games
9. He is Chilean
10. The Hull City Tigers
11. Pablo Zabaleta managed to get 11 yellow cards in the 35 league games he played this season
12. West Ham
13. He played 963 games
14. The score was 6 – 0 to Chelsea
15. The referee sent off Kieran Gibbs instead of Alex Oxlade-Chamberlain in a case of mistaken identity
16. Seamus Coleman
17. Juan Mata
18. It was Mohamed Salah
19. Tim Krull
20. He managed 27 wins

Quiz 23: 2014 – 15 Season Answers

1. Chelsea
2. Swansea
3. It was Chevrolet
4. Gus Poyet
5. Sergio Aguero topped the list with 26 goals. Harry Kane got 21 goals and Diego Costa 20 goals
6. It was Mario Balotelli
7. Ryan Bertrand
8. It was Stoke
9. Steven Gerrard
10. It was Sadio Mane
11. He played 491 Premier League games
12. Sunderland
13. Lee Catermole
14. Moussa Sissoko
15. John Terry
16. Sunderland. Nine of them were 0 – 0 draws
17. The goal was against Chelsea when he was playing for Man City
18. It was 274 days
19. It was Cesc Fabregas with 18 assists
20. Angel Di Maria is Argentinian

Quiz 24: 2015 – 16 Season Answers

1. 5,000 – 1
2. Nigel Pearson
3. Greece lost 1 – 0 at home to the Faroe Islands
4. He beat Ruud van Nistelrooy's record who scored in 10 consecutive games for Man Utd in the 2003 – 04 season
5. Swansea
6. Sunderland
7. It was Wolfsburg

8. He is Belgian
9. They had won 4 and were one point from the relegation zone
10. Bayer Leverkusen
11. Victor Wanyama
12. They led for a total of 243 minutes and gained 3 wins
13. Arsenal. He was impersonating Alexis Sanchez
14. Adam Lallana
15. It took 19 games
16. Sergio Aguero
17. 10 points
18. Arsenal
19. Jack Grealish
20. It was a bomb scare. A practice security routine had left a dummy 'bomb' at Old Trafford and a controlled explosion was carried out

Quiz 25: 2016 – 17 Season Answers

1. They finished 12th
2. It was Burnley who finished 16th
3. £30
4. Chelsea
5. It was Tottenham. Their goal difference was 8 goals better than Chelsea, but they finished 8 points behind them and in second place
6. Man Utd
7. It was Chelsea who won the Cup Winners in 1970 – 71, the Champions League in 2011 – 12 and the Europa League in 2016 – 17
8. It was Craig Shakespeare
9. Swansea
10. It was Romelu Lukaku with 25 goals. Sanchez got 24 goals and Aguero 20 goals
11. He got 4. They were against West Brom, Stoke, Leicester and Hull

12. Middlesbrough only got 27 compared to Kane's 29
13. Juventus
14. It was Mike Phelan
15. They were all headers. The first player to achieve this since Duncan Ferguson in 1997
16. It was Chelsea
17. They beat Crystal Palace 2 – 0 at Selhurst Park. They drew against Hull and Man Utd away
18. Shanghai SIPG
19. It was Harry Kane in a 2 – 1 win over Man Utd
20. Crystal Palace paid Newcastle a reported £12m

Quiz 26: 2017 – 18 Season Answers

1. They won by 19 points
2. Man Utd
3. Alliance Tyres
4. American
5. It was Darren Moore who was appointed caretaker manager on the 2nd April 2018 upon the sacking of Alan Pardew and were 10 points from safety. They then went unbeaten in April earning him the Manager of the Month
6. Bournemouth averaged 10,640 spectators, Watford averaged 20,231 and Swansea 20,623
7. Wigan beat them 1 – 0
8. He was sacked on the 11th September 2017 and lasted 4 games. They lost them all without scoring a goal
9. It was 3 teams – Brighton, Man Utd and Swansea
10. He won 3 and drew 5, losing the rest
11. They beat Stoke 1 – 0
12. It was reported as £75m
13. He came from Roma
14. It was Cesar Azpilicueta who scored an own goal, though Palace did go on to win 2 – 1
15. He scored 17 goals in 33 games

16. West Ham
17. He is Chilean
18. The score was 5 – 0
19. Borussia Dortmund
20. They scored 106 goals

Quiz 27: 2018 – 19 Season Answers

1. It was Liverpool
2. They lost only 1 game
3. It was Tottenham who were playing at Wembley till the new ground was completed. They got 81,332 to watch their game against Arsenal on the 2nd March 2019
4. He took 7.69 seconds
5. He was signed from Roma
6. He is Brazilian
7. They lost 3 – 2 to Crystal Place
8. It was Pierre-Emerick Aubameyang
9. Lucas Moura
10. It was the Kirklees Stadium. Dean Court was Bournemouth's Stadium and the Falmer Stadium was Brighton's
11. It was Trent Alexander – Arnold
12. Molde
13. It was Liverpool who lost 2 – 1 to Man City
14. The goalkeeper Kepa Arrizabalaga refused to come off when subbed by Maurizio Sarri
15. Ryan Sessegnon
16. It was Chelsea who lost 6 – 0 to Man City in February 2019. This was despite having beaten them 2 – 0 at Stamford Bridge in December
17. Man Utd were top on the first day when they beat Leicester in the opening game on the Friday night
18. They built Wolves twice
19. It was Chelsea
20. It was Connor Coady of Wolves

Quiz 28: 2019 – 20 Season Answers

1. They were 22 points ahead
2. Man City had scored 71 goals, Liverpool 66 goals and Leicester 58 goals
3. It was Leicester
4. It was Watford who beat them 3 – 0
5. There were 5 – Arsenal, Chelsea, Crystal Palace, Tottenham and West Ham
6. It was American Express. LoveBet were with Burnley and Vitality were Bournemouth's shirt sponsor
7. Ben Mee
8. They won by 18 points
9. Jordan Henderson
10. It was Arsenal who had 86 yellow cards and they also had the most red cards with 5
11. It was Ederson who had 16 clean sheets for Man City
12. Raheem Sterling. He got one against West Ham and another against Brighton
13. He turned 72 on the very first day of the season
14. There were 7 remaining beating Man City, Man Utd and Everton who had all won with 5 games remaining. It was also the latest by date being in June
15. It is 6 teams – Liverpool, Arsenal, Tottenham, Everton, Man Utd and Chelsea
16. They didn't manage more than 2 all season
17. It was Jack Grealish who was fouled 167 times
18. They won 14 penalties
19. On the 21st September 2019 Man City beat Watford 8 – 0
20. The 2015 – 16 season

Quiz 29: Miscellaneous 1 Answers

1. It was Oldham who finished 14th in Division 2
2. There were no corners

3. Wayne Rooney with 208 goals
4. Steve Bruce has been promoted four times – twice with Hull and twice with Birmingham
5. Petr Cech with 202
6. It was Niall Quinn on August 19th 1992 playing for Man City against Middlesbrough
7. Cristiano Ronaldo scored the 1,000th Premier League for Man Utd against Middlesbrough in 2005 – 06
8. Neville Southall missed out on scoring. Friedel scored for Blackburn against Charlton and Robinson for Tottenham against Watford
9. Costa Rican
10. Man City
11. Everton which was named after the local Methodist church
12. It was Gordon Strachan who scored a hat trick for Leeds against Blackburn on the 10th April 1993
13. It was Gary Speed
14. It was Eriksson who was appointed on the 6th July 2007
15. He called him a voyeur
16. They had negative goal difference of 4 goals
17. It was Oldham
18. It was QPR who finished 5th
19. A trick question as unfortunately for Middlesbrough all three happened
20. Roy Hodgson

Quiz 30: Miscellaneous 2 Answers

1. 175 goals
2. He is Ukrainian
3. It was Peter Schmeichel when he scored against Everton in October 2001
4. West Ham. It is the lyrics of 'I'm forever blowing bubbles'
5. Michael Owen
6. Leicester

7. It is Aston Villa
8. It was Neil Sullivan playing for Wimbledon
9. It was Brad Friedel
10. Clive Mendonca
11. There were 13
12. Bryan Robson
13. He won 6 games
14. Preston
15. Facundo Sava
16. Tottenham. Sullivan played 2000 – 03 and Keller 2001 – 05
17. Kieron Dyer
18. It is Turf Moor which has been used by Burnley since 1883
19. Thierry Henry scored 175 goals
20. In November 2009 Defoe scored 5 goals in the second half in Tottenham's 9 – 1 thrashing of Wigan

Printed in Great Britain
by Amazon